NATURAL ENVIRONMENT RESEARCH COUNCIL

INSTITUTE OF GEOLOGICAL SCIENCES

Geological Survey and Museum

BRITISH REGIONAL GEOLOGY

London
and Thames Valley

by

R. L. SHERLOCK, D.SC., A.R.C.S.

THIRD EDITION

with some additions by

R. CASEY, PH.D., S. C. A. HOLMES, M.A.

AND

V. WILSON, PH.D., M.SC., D.I.C.

LONDON

HER MAJESTY'S STATIONERY OFFICE

1960

The Institute of Geological Sciences was formed by the incorporation of the Geological Survey of Great Britain and the Museum of Practical Geology with Overseas Geological Surveys and is a constituent body of the Natural Environment Research Council

First published	*1935*
Third edition	*1960*
Fifth impression	
(*with amendments*)	*1976*

ISBN 011 880192 9

CONTENTS

ILLUSTRATIONS

FIGURES IN TEXT

PLATES

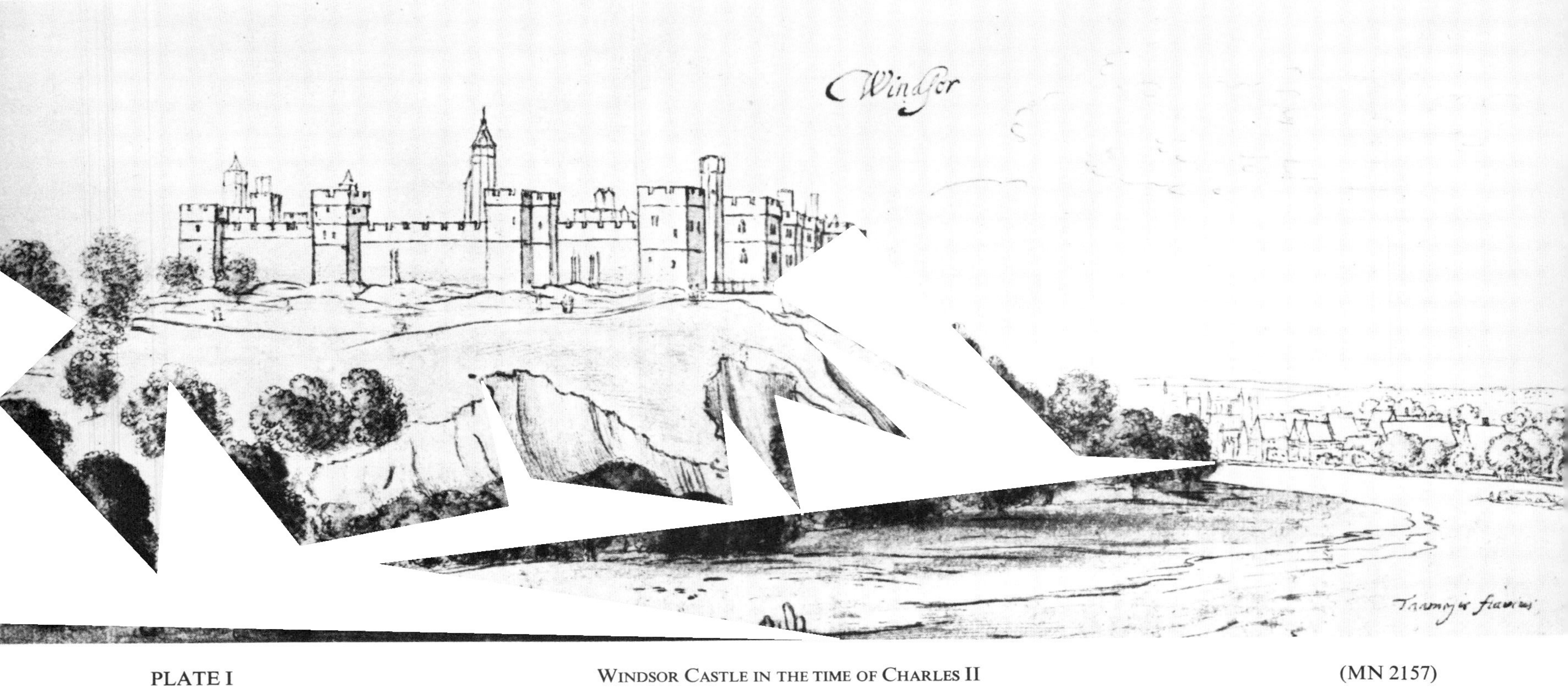

PLATE I

WINDSOR CASTLE IN THE TIME OF CHARLES II

After a drawing by Hollar in the Royal Library at Windsor Castle

Reproduced by gracious permission of H.M. the Queen

(MN 2157)

LONDON AND THAMES VALLEY

I. INTRODUCTION

Boundary of the Region.—The region described in this handbook includes the entire counties of Essex, Hertfordshire, Middlesex, Buckinghamshire, Berkshire, and Oxfordshire, and parts of Wiltshire, Hampshire, Surrey, and Kent. The northern boundary is that of the counties as far as a point near Chippenham, Wiltshire. Here it meets the southern boundary, which is a curved line commencing at Chatham and passing north of Sevenoaks and Reigate as far as Guildford ; it then follows the junction of the Eocene and Chalk formations westward until the Eocene fails, whence the boundary extends across country, through Calne, to the limit of Wiltshire. This is shown in Fig. 1, p. 2.

Historical.—Although, in old books, there are numerous references to geological facts relating to the London and Thames Valley region, the earliest systematic account of the geology is to be found in the works of Sir J. Prestwich, who, in a series of papers published between 1847 and 1854 in the *Quarterly Journal of the Geological Society*, gave a full account of the Eocene deposits. R. W. Mylne published a *Map of the Geology and Contours of London and its Environs* in 1856. In 1861 W. Whitaker, who joined the Geological Survey in 1857, published a paper on the *Geology of Reading*, in the *Geologist*, which inaugurated a series of papers on the area that, collectively, form the most important addition to the knowledge of London geology since the work of Prestwich. Whitaker summarized his own work and that of other geologists in several memoirs published by the Geological Survey, including *The Geology of the London Basin*, 1872, and *The Geology of London and of part of the Thames Valley*, 2 vols., 1889. The second of these works included an account of the superficial deposits (Drifts) which had been omitted from the earlier book. A smaller *Guide to the Geology of London and the Neighbourhood*, by Whitaker, first published by the Survey in 1875, reached a 6th edition in 1901, and was then superseded, in 1909, by *The Geology of the London District* by H. B. Woodward, and this in turn was revised by C. E. N. Bromehead in 1922. Professor P. G. H. Boswell has also added much to our knowledge of the area (see *Quarterly Journal of the Geological Society*, vol. 71, for 1915). Of late years a great deal of information on London geology has been collected, largely by members of the Geologists' Association, and published, for the most part, in the *Proceedings of the Geologists' Association* and the *Geological Magazine*.

The original Geological Survey maps of the whole area are hand-coloured and were surveyed directly on a 1 in. to the mile scale. About half of them were published in two editions, Drift and Solid, the others (chiefly the western ones) in the Solid edition only. A New Series set of maps is available. For these the area is surveyed on a 6 in. to the mile scale and the geology is printed in colour on the 1 in. to the mile maps. So far sheets covering London and most of its

FIG. 1.—*Outline map of the area with sites of deep borings. The formation indicated is that in which the boring ends.* Nos. 14 *and* 25 *may possibly end in early Carboniferous strata*

1 Burford
2 Witney (Apley Barn)
3 Faringdon
4 Noke
5 Steeple Aston
6 Marsh Gibbon
7 Calvert
8 Charndon
9 Twyford
10 Tattenhoe
11 Little Missenden
12 Bushey
13 Ware
14 Turnford
15 Southall
16 Willesden
17 Chiswick
18 Richmond
19 Kentish Town
20 Tottenham Court Road, London
21 Streatham
22 Beckton
23 Crossness
24 Warlingham
25 Fobbing
26 Cliffe Marshes
27 Cliffe Nos. 10 & 11
28 Bobbing
29 Sheerness
30 Canvey Island
31 Harwich
32 Weeley

outer suburbs, also Oxford and parts of Berkshire, Buckinghamshire, Kent, Surrey, Hampshire and Wiltshire have been issued. MS. copies of 6-in. scale maps are available for consultation in the Geological Survey Library. There have also been issued four miles to the inch colour-printed maps of the whole area. Besides Memoirs on 1-in. maps an account of the water-supply from underground sources of each county has been published by the Geological Survey.

Physical Features.—The main feature of the region is the Chalk escarpment which, entering the area near Calne, extends continuously through Wiltshire, Berkshire, Oxfordshire, Buckinghamshire, and then in and out of Bedfordshire and Huntingdonshire until it passes out of the district into Cambridgeshire, near Royston.

The Chalk ridge has no general name to the west of the Goring Gap, through which the Thames passes, but north and east of the river it is known as the Chiltern Hills. Some of the highest points west of the Goring Gap are Hackpen Hill, 887 ft., and Whitehorse Hill, 856 ft.; and in the Chiltern Hills 837 ft. opposite Watlington, 840 ft. at Combe Hill, Halton, and 811 ft. opposite Ivinghoe. The ridge declines in elevation from Combe Hill until, near Royston, its summit is about 525 ft. above Ordnance Datum.

The escarpment faces a little north of east near Calne, then swings round gradually until it faces a little west of north in Berkshire. The direction of the Chiltern Hills is from south-west to north-east. The variation in direction indicates a difference in the strike of the strata.

To the west, beyond the Chalk ridge, there is a succession of valleys and ridges, the latter formed by limestones and sandstones, the former by clays. Owing to the discontinuous character of most of these rocks the ridges and valleys are also discontinuous. Moreover, some cross-faulting, bringing different rocks into line, helps to break the regularity of the features. The highest elevation beyond the chalk ridge is Oatley Hill, on the Oxfordshire boundary, which reaches 795 ft. above O.D. and is capped by Great Oolite.

The Chalk escarpment is broken in places by valleys, the chief being that of the Thames at Goring. Other gaps are at Wendover, Tring, Luton, and Hitchin.

Considerably within the Chalk escarpment, that is towards London, there are remains of a much lower parallel ridge made by the margin of the overlying Eocene strata. The rocks, however, are soft and incoherent and the ridge is so broken and overridden by superficial deposits that it can scarcely be called an escarpment. It is seen between Cookham and Wargrave (about 450 ft.), Tilehurst, Cold Ash (485 ft.), and Fox Hill, near Inkpen.

The remainder of the region comprises the middle of the London Basin, an area covered by rocks newer than the Chalk. This area owes its physical features primarily to its synclinal structure and secondarily to the layer of superficial deposits which cover the greater part of Essex and form numerous isolated patches west of the River Lea. Essex consists of a low plateau cut up by numerous rivers and sloping gently down to the North Sea and the Thames estuary. Along the river and estuary there is a strip of silt, edged by strips of river gravel forming terraces.

The greater part of the region is drained by the Thames and its tributaries. Exceptions are the northern half of Buckinghamshire, which is drained by the

Ouse, and the eastern half of Essex, drained directly into the North Sea by the Chelmer, Blackwater, Colne, and Stour.

Geological Formations.—The larger divisions of strata present in the area are (Fig. 2, p. 5) as follows :—

Quaternary	Recent and Pleistocene
Tertiary	Eocene
Mesozoic (=Secondary)	{ Cretaceous Jurassic

Besides these a number of older formations (Palaeozoic) have been found in deep borings (Fig. 1, p. 2). It appears that within the London Basin the strata down to and including the Gault are always present, but this latter formation rests on a variety of rocks, many of them not seen at the surface anywhere in the area. In the middle of the basin the Gault rests unconformably on folded and denuded Silurian and Devonian strata—the ' Palaeozoic Floor ' as it is called. On the northern flank of this floor there is a succession beneath the Gault down to the Middle Jurassic, but on the southern flank a thick mass of freshwater beds, the Wealden Series, intervenes between the Lower Greensand and the Jurassic formations (Fig. 24, p. 57).

The presence or absence of the Lower Greensand beneath the Gault is of importance for water supplies. This formation thins out against the Palaeozoic rocks and is missing beneath most of Essex and between London and Hertford. The area that is devoid of Lower Greensand is bounded by a line entering the district a little north of Bishop's Stortford, extending to a point between Slough and Southall, then turning east to pass a little north of Streatham and crossing the Thames close to Crossness, and finally passing out to sea near Tilbury.

Structure.—The district is comparatively free from folding and faulting. Of the tectonic features, as they are termed, the chief is the syncline known as the London Basin (Fig. 24, p. 57), extending from Savernake Forest in the west into the North Sea in the east. A fold comprises both a trough (syncline) and ridge (anticline), and the complete fold in this case is wider than our district, the greater part of the axis of the ridge lying in the Weald, beyond our southern boundary. In the present case the ridge in part of its course is a monocline instead of an anticline, *i.e.* the strata having risen out of the syncline remain nearly horizontal instead of falling quickly again on the other side of the ridge.

The southern bounding ridge of the London Basin becomes very strongly developed in the Hogs Back, between Farnham and Guildford, so much so that it has broken and become faulted both along (strike) and across (dip) the axis. Both strike and dip faults were produced by compressive forces and it is interesting to note that the strike faults are reversed (thrust) faults, the southern part of the strata having been pushed over the northern part (Fig. 3, p. 6). The bounding ridge is not a single continuous one but a line of ridges slightly *en echelon*. The most westerly ridge, the Vale of Pewsey anticline, borders the area from south of Marlborough to Farnham, where it ends and is replaced by the Hogs Back monocline, which dies out eastward.

A line of small domes (or very short anticlines), collectively known as the Islip anticline, is traceable from Shellingford, near Faringdon, and extends to the north-east of Oxford as far as Calvert, Bucks. The arching of the strata is but slight.

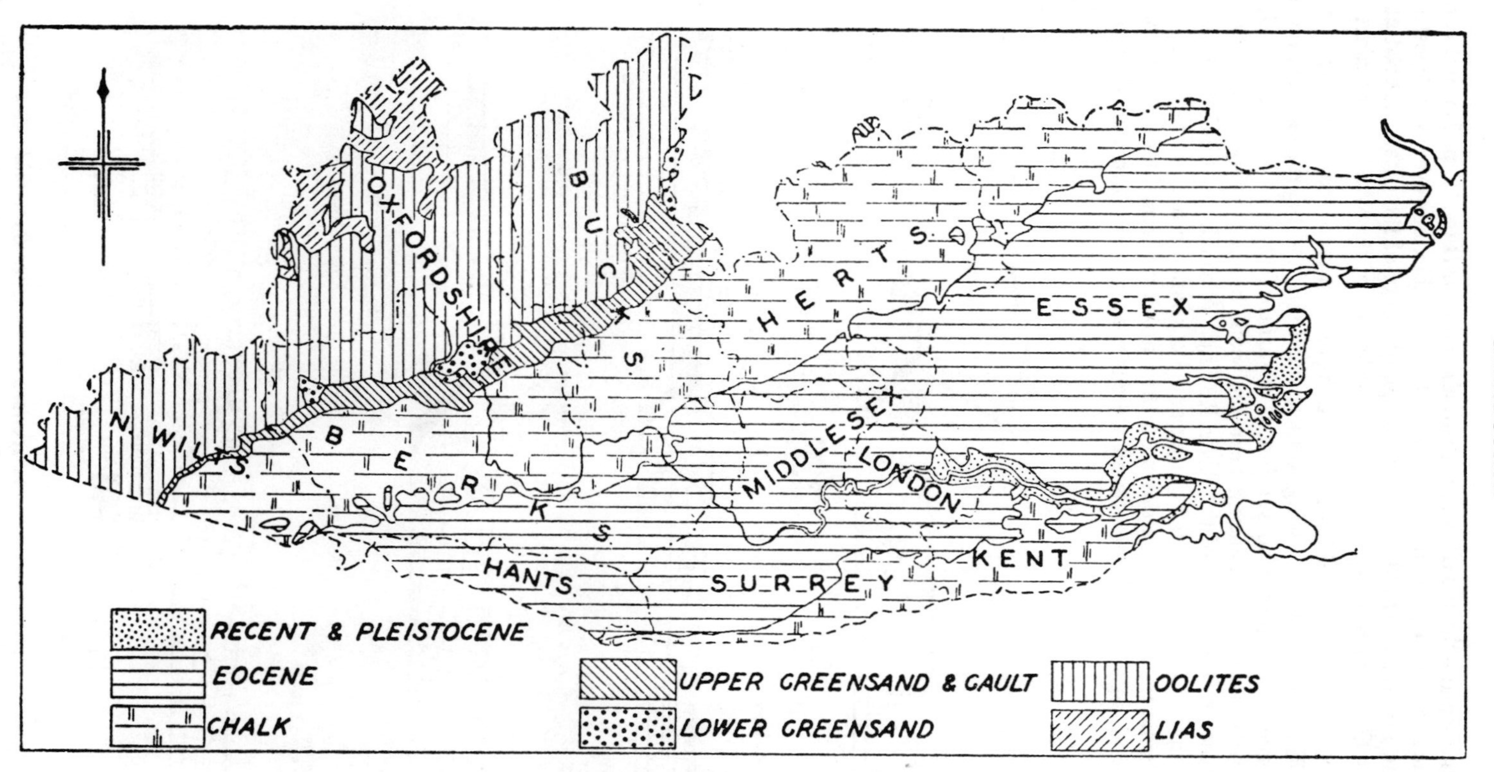

FIG. 2.—*Sketch-map of the geology of the area*

Another anticlinal axis passes through Windsor (Fig. 11, p. 27), but cannot be followed for more than a few miles. It is possible, however, as suggested by the late Dr. W. J. Arkell, that the change of strike of the Chalk noticed at the Goring Gap may be caused by a ridge on the line of the Windsor anticline.

A number of minor folds and faults have been recorded in the area. They are difficult to follow far owing to their small size and the incoherent strata of the Eocene preventing the development of surface features. A definite fault, the Greenwich Fault, commencing hear Dulwich, has a curving course through Greenwich to the mouth of the River Roding. A roughly parallel fault extends from Raynes Park, through Tooting and Peckham, to die out near Deptford. Both faults throw the strata down on their north-western sides. The Deptford Fault ends in a small dome. Small anticlines are also known extending north-

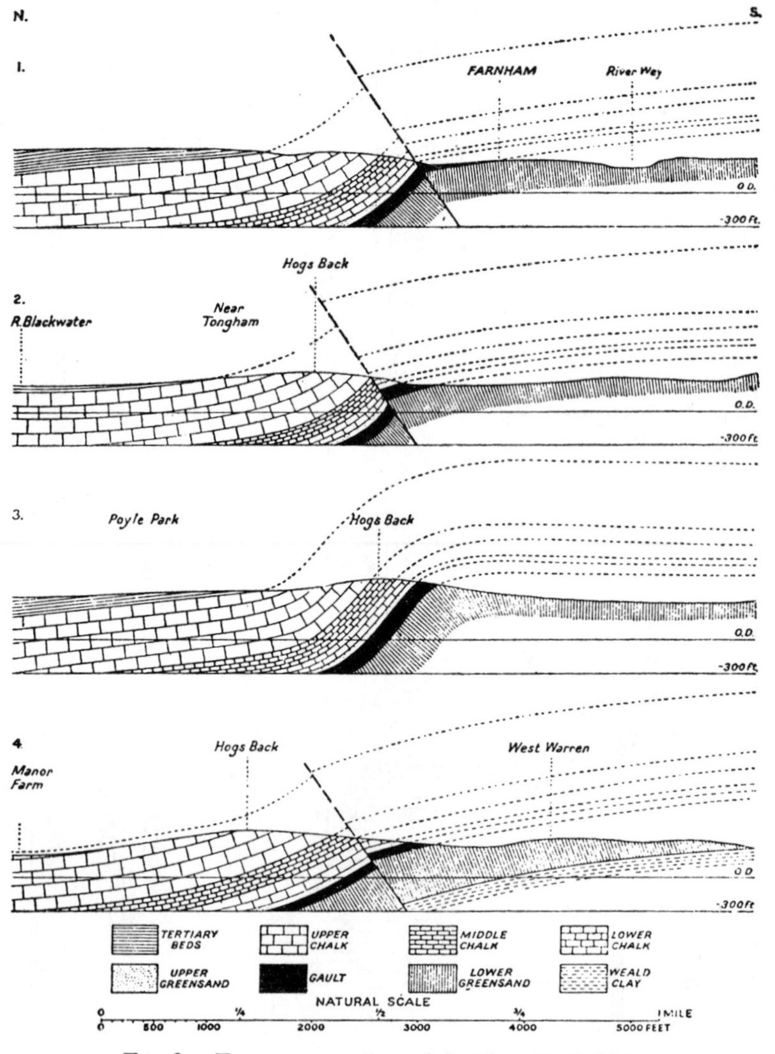

FIG. 3.—*Transverse sections of the Hogs Back fold*

west to south-east ; one through Ewell, another through Bromley, and there are others.

The middle of the London Basin is diversified by folding, which trends mainly north-east or east-north-east. A syncline through Acton towards Hornsey, for instance, is in line with a deep trough on the south-west near Chertsey and Twickenham. Prof. S. W. Wooldridge has pointed out a monoclinal fold along the Lea Valley through Cheshunt. Professor P. G. H. Boswell thought it probable that there is an important north and south fault passing Billericay on the east side, and also a north-east and south-west fault extending from near Chelmsford to near Harwich, passing about four miles to the south of Colchester. Boreholes have proved that the strata are certainly folded in these areas.

On the northern boundary of the region there may be, as pointed out by the late Dr. R. H. Rastall, a north-west to south-east anticlinal axis of pre- or early Cretaceous age, passing west of Leighton Buzzard and causing the abrupt termination of the Lower Greensand at that place. There is a definite small fault throwing down to the east, crossing the Chesham Branch Railway a mile east of Chesham, and a small trough fault at Leverstock Green, also extending north and south. A remarkable trough-fault crosses the Eocene outlier of Lane End, west of High Wycombe, in a north-west to south-east direction. Other doubtful folds have been recorded, but all are small and their directions are still uncertain.

The dates of the folding (orogenic activity) are estimated by the ages of the rocks disturbed or undisturbed. Thus, the fault at Chesham must be newer than the Chalk because it disturbs that formation. On this principle the supposed ridge west of Leighton Buzzard will be of pre-Cretaceous and post-Liassic age. The Chalk was evidently uplifted and eroded before the Eocene deposits were laid down over it, but the main period of the folding to be observed was probably coëval with the development of the Alps, that is considerably later than the formation of the London Clay, in fact during the Miocene period, which is unrepresented by strata in Britain. It is possible that minor folding continues at intervals and that such events as the Colchester earthquake are indications of minor orogenic activity.

The structure of the ancient rocks that underlie the London Basin is referred to below (p. 8).

II. PALAEOZOIC FORMATIONS

THE Palaeozoic rocks present below the formations listed above (p. 4) were subjected to many earth movements before the Jurassic and Cretaceous rocks were formed, besides taking part in later movements. Dependent as we are on deep borings for information, only a general idea can be obtained as to the distribution of the old formations.

It is known that Upper Cambrian rocks underlie Jurassic rocks at Calvert. Silurian strata were met with in North Kent, at two boreholes near Harwich, and at Ware ; at Cliffe the rocks were dated as of Wenlock age, and at Little Missenden they were stated to be Downtonian. Various boreholes in London, Middlesex, Buckinghamshire and Hertfordshire, reached old rocks including Devonian and Old Red Sandstone, which was recognised as being of Upper Old Red Sandstone age at Southall ; Upper Devonian rocks were found under Tottenham Court Road, London ; Late Devonian or Early Carboniferous rocks were encountered at Turnford and at Fobbing ; Upper Carboniferous strata were entered at Burford. The sites of selected boreholes reaching the Palaeozoic strata are shown in Fig. 1 (p. 2).

More recent boreholes have added details to our knowledge of the Palaeozoic floor. Two in Surrey, at Warlingham and Shalford proved respectively Lower Carboniferous and Silurian rocks of Upper Llandovery age. At Noke Hill in Oxfordshire, Upper Old Red Sandstone was reached. A further borehole at Burford proved Upper Coal Measures and one at Faringdon, in Berkshire, entered Lower Old Red Sandstone. At Canvey Island a borehole has also proved Old Red Sandstone.

The shape of the surface of the mass of Palaeozoic rocks on which the newer strata rest is of scientific and economic importance. The Palaeozoic formations had been accumulated, folded, depressed and raised again through geological ages, before the Mesozoic rocks were deposited on the planed-off edges of these older beds. Evidence of the shape of the surface on which the Mesozoic strata were deposited is obtained from borings and from determinations of variations in gravity at different places. It appears that the surface is flattish, forming a tilted platform, from about 1,500 to 500 ft. below sea-level over the greater part of the area, but that in North Buckinghamshire it rises to about 150 ft. below sea-level and in North Oxfordshire even to less than 80 ft. The general flatness of the surface indicates that the greater part has not been subject to sub-aerial erosion after it was planed down by the sea. The platform must, however, have been affected by the fold-movements that occurred after the newer rocks had been deposited.

Most of the older Palaeozoic rocks discovered in the borings are similar to those now exposed in the Welsh Border country.

III. THE JURASSIC SYSTEM

THE Jurassic rocks cover the north-western part of the area, comprising a strip of Wiltshire round Malmesbury and Swindon, a narrow strip of Berkshire, the more northerly two-thirds of Oxfordshire, together with parts of Buckinghamshire lying north of Thame and Aylesbury. The strata consist of limestones and clays with occasional sands or sandstones.

The strata were laid down in shallow water not far from the land. Their marked local variations may be ascribed to a great extent to this fact, but in addition there were minor warpings of the earth's crust which resulted in small breaks in the succession of deposits owing to the erosion of ridges and accumulation of sediment in hollows. The nearness to land also resulted in the formation of estuarine and shallow-water reef conditions in places, and the highest strata, the Purbeck Beds, were deposited in fresh water.

Owing to the extreme local variation in Jurassic strata, and especially in the Lower and Middle Oolites, it is difficult to give a table of strata that accords with all parts of the area ; the table on page 11 is therefore a generalized succession.

The Jurassic strata thin out towards the south-east under the cover of newer rocks, as has been proved in boreholes. This indicates the presence during the Jurassic period of land in that direction.

Many Jurassic rocks are highly fossiliferous and this has enabled them to be subdivided in great detail into zones characterized by different fossils, and in particular by different ammonites. The Jurassic period has been called the ' Age of Reptiles,' and it also saw the evolution of the earliest known bird and some of the earliest mammals. The bones of *Ceteosaurus oxoniensis* Phillips, a reptile 60 ft. long, have been found at Bletchington Station.

LOWER JURASSIC (=LIAS)

In this district the Lias occurs at the surface only in the northern part of Oxfordshire. It is essentially a clay formation with thick argillaceous limestones towards the base. At Banbury there is a bed of limestone about 1 ft. thick which takes a good polish and is known as the ' Banbury Marble '. It is crowded with shells and belongs to the Lower Lias. In North Oxfordshire the Marlstone Rock Bed at the top of the Middle Lias is developed as an economic iron ore. Where it is found beneath a thick cover of Upper Lias clay it is a bluish-green oolitic rock, but near the surface it is weathered to a soft, brown, rusty-looking stone. It occurs at Fawler, Adderbury, Hook Norton, etc., mostly north and north-east of Banbury. The iron content is from 17 to 31.2 per cent. On the Edge Hill plateau the Marlstone Rock Bed is a rusty sandstone quarried for road-mending, building and ornamental purposes, when it is known as Hornton Stone. The Upper Lias reaches a minimum at Fawler, where there is only from 5 to 12 ft. of unfossiliferous clay with a thin basal limestone band crowded with ammonites (W. J. Arkell).

The following are a few common fossils from the Lias :—

LOWER LIAS.—Ammonite : *Androgynoceras capricornum.* Belemnite :

Passaloteuthis apicicurvatus. Lamellibranchs: *Oxytoma inaequivalve*; *Pleuromya costata; Modiolus scalprus.*

MIDDLE LIAS (Lower part).—Ammonite: *Amaltheus margaritatus.* Lamellibranchs: *Entolium liasianum*; *Protocardia truncata*; *Pronoella intermedia.*

MIDDLE LIAS (Upper part=Marlstone Rock Bed).—Ammonite: *Pleuroceras spinatum.* Lamellibranch : *Aequipecten aequivalvis.* Brachiopods : *Lobothyris punctata* ; *Tetrarhynchia tetrahedra.*

UPPER LIAS.—Ammonites : *Harpoceras mulgravium* ; *Dactylioceras gracile*; *Hildaites levisoni.* Belemnite; *Acrocoelites* sp. Lamellibranch: *Astarte obsoleta.*

MIDDLE JURASSIC (=LOWER OOLITES)

The variable character of the Lower Oolites is due to their deposition in shallow water subject to rapid changes of currents and other conditions. Eroded surfaces and non-sequences are also indications of these conditions.

Inferior Oolite.—This formation is particularly thin as compared with that of the regions to the west and south-west and passes into sandy deposits towards the north-east.

Great Oolite.—The Chipping Norton Limestone is employed for dry walling and road-metal. It contains remains of the giant reptile *Ceteosaurus oxoniensis.* The Stonesfield Slate is a sandy limestone and is called a slate only because it has been worked for roofing buildings since the Roman occupation. Palaeontologically it is very important because it contains amongst other fossils, the jaws and teeth of small mammals. In Oxfordshire there are estuarine limestones and marls about 25 ft. thick, known as the Neaeran Beds (from the shell formerly called *Neaera*), below the Stonesfield Slate. They include some thin limestones and marl covered by a fresh-water marl with a basal pebble bed and containing *Viviparus.* Above the Neaeran Beds there is locally some Fuller's Earth. These beds are limited in extent and very variable. The Great Oolite Limestones comprise, as a rule, a lower division of sandy and oolitic flags and current-bedded oolites, and an upper division of soft, earthy limestone and marls. A freestone has been extensively worked at Taynton, near Burford.

Bradford Clay.—The Bradford Clay (named after Bradford-on-Avon) appears at the surface at West Kington, where it is a fossiliferous marly clay only a few feet thick. It has also been recorded in deep borings at Richmond and Tottenham Court Road.

Forest Marble.—This formation takes its name from Wychwood Forest. The name is unfortunate, for as the late Dr. W. J. Arkell has pointed out, the limestone worked was obtained from below and not from above the Bradford Clay. For a long time this limestone was polished for ' marble ' chimney-pieces, but the name Forest Marble is now given to a group of very variable strata including clay beds.

Cornbrash.—The Cornbrash is a rubbly and usually highly fossiliferous limestone so-named because it gives rise to ' brashy ' or rubbly soils well suited

TABLE OF JURASSIC STRATA

					Thickness Ft.
Upper Jurassic	Upper Oolites		Purbeck Beds : Limestone, sometimes oolitic, and marl	about	10
			Portland Beds : Creamy, rubbly limestone and buff fine sands . . .	,,	40
			Kimmeridge Clay : Dark clay or shale, very fossiliferous	,,	150 to 300
	Middle Oolites	Corallian	Upper Calcareous Grit; Coral Rag: Oolitic limestone; Lower Calcareous Grit = Ampthill Clay	,,	80 to 100
			Oxford Clay : Grey clay; Kellaways Beds : Sandy and loamy beds with "doggers". Up to 60 ft.	,,	450 to 575
Middle Jurassic	Lower Oolites		Cornbrash : Rubbly limestone . . .	,,	2 to 20
			Forest Marble : False-bedded shelly oolitic limestones with clay . .		12 to 50
			Bradford Clay (local)		2 to 3
		Great Oolite Series about 130 ft.	Great Oolite Limestones : Oolitic or earthy limestones and marl	about	50 to 100
			Stonesfield Slate : Grey sandy and oolitic limestone . . .	,,	4 to 88
			Fuller's Earth and Neaeran Beds (local)	up to	25
			Chipping Norton Limestone : Oolitic and sandy slabby limestone	,,	30
		Inferior Oolite Series	Clypeus Grit : Rubbly oolitic marls and course marly oolites	about	20 to 35
			Upper Trigonia Grit : Oolitic, also iron-shot limestones .	,,	13
			scissum Beds	,,	7 to 10
Lower Jurassic	Lias (about 627 ft.)		Upper Lias : Clays with thin basal limestones	,,	5 to 100
			Middle Lias : Marlstone Rock Bed .	,,	1 to 25
			Middle Lias : Silts and silty clay .	,,	20 to 80
			Lower Lias : Clays with argillaceous limestones in lower part . . .	,,	450

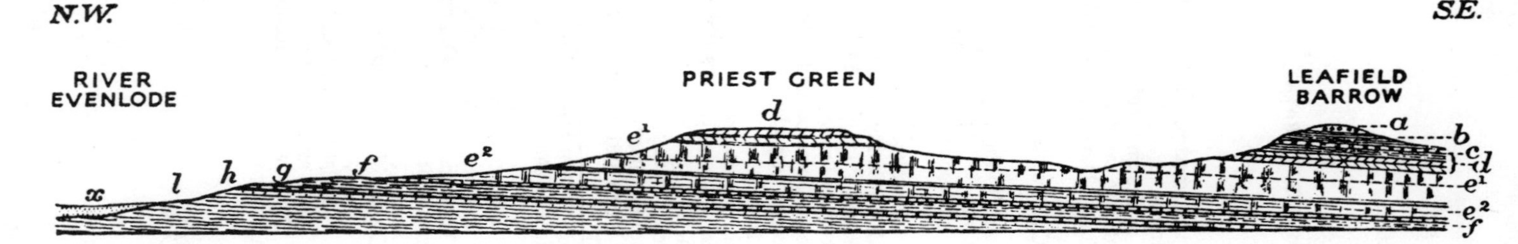

FIG. 4.—*Section from the River Evenlode to Leafield Barrow* (E. Hull), *showing the general succession of formations from the Lower Lias to the Oxford Clay*

Horizontal Scale, 3 in. to 1 mile. Vertical, 6 in. to 1 mile.

x=Low-level gravel.
a=High-level gravel.
b=Oxford Clay.
c=Cornbrash.

d=Forest Marble (including Kemble Beds).
e—*e*¹=Upper zone of Great Oolite.
—*e*²=Lower zone of Great Oolite.

f=Inferior Oolite.
g=Upper Lias Clay.
h=Marlstone Rock Bed.
i=Lower Lias.

to the growth of corn. Although never more than 25 ft. thick and frequently much less, it is the most constant subdivision of the Lower Oolites. Near Oxford the Cornbrash is markedly unconformable to the Forest Marble. Thin as it is, it consists of Upper and Lower subdivisions each characterized by distinctive faunas.

The Lower Oolite fossils include a great array of molluscs (ammonites, belemnites, gastropods and lamellibranchs), brachiopods, corals and sea-urchins. A few common or important species are the following :—

INFERIOR OOLITE.—Ammonite : *Leioceras opalinum.* Lamellibranchs : *Pholadomya fidicula, Trigonia costata, Modiolus (Inoperna) plicatus, Lopha flabelloides.* Brachiopod : *Tubithyris globata.* Coral : *Isastraea conybearei.*

GREAT OOLITE (Chipping Norton Limestone).—Ammonite : *Oppelia (Oxycerites) limosa.* Lamellibranchs : *Lucina bellona, Ostrea (Liostrea) subrugulosa.*

GREAT OOLITE (Neaeran Beds).—Lamellibranchs : *Cuspidaria* (' *Neaera* ') *ibbetsoni, Bakevellia waltoni.* Gastropod (marine) : *Cossmannea (Eunerinea) bathonica.* Gastropod (non-marine) : *Viviparus (Bathonella) scotica.*

GREAT OOLITE (Stonesfield Slate).—Cycad-like plant : *Ptilophyllum acutifolium.* Lamellibranchs : *Trigonia (Vaugonia) impressa, Gervillella ovata.* Reptile : *Rhamphocephalus prestwichi.*

BRADFORD CLAY.—Brachiopod : *Digonella digona.*

FOREST MARBLE.—Lamellibranchs : *Modiolus imbricatus, Costigervillia crassicosta.* Brachiopod : *Epithyris marmorea.* Echinoid : *Acrosalenia hemicidaroides.*

CORNBRASH (Lower).—Ammonite : *Clydoniceras discus.* Lamellibranch : *Meleagrinella echinata.* Brachiopods : *Cererithyris intermedia, Obovothyris obovata.* Echinoid : *Nucleolites orbicularis.*

CORNBRASH (Upper).—Ammonite : *Macrocephalites (Kamptokephalites), hudlestoni.* Lamellibranch : *Trigonia elongata.* Brachiopod : *Microthyridina lagenalis.*

UPPER JURASSIC (=MIDDLE AND UPPER OOLITES)

Kellaways Beds.—These are sandy and loamy strata with ' doggers,' that is concretionary masses of calcareous sandstone. Usually there is a bed of clay at the base. In this region they are rarely seen and are probably poorly developed. They usually form a marshy belt of country.

Oxford Clay.—The Oxford Clay, from which the Kellaways Beds are scarcely separable owing to the gradual passage from one to the other, is a bluish or grey clay turning brown on weathering. Bedding is often obscure, especially in the upper part, and is marked only by septaria and thin layers of earthy limestone. Below, however, the rock is more or less shaly. Selenite (crystallized hydrated sulphate of lime, *i.e.* gypsum) and iron-pyrites are abundant. From Leighton Buzzard eastward the upper part of the Oxford Clay is covered by Lower Greensand and Gault. The general relations of the various divisions of the Jurassic System up to the Oxford Clay are shown in Fig. 4, p. 12.

Corallian.—The Corallian strata are a variable series of sands, sandy oolitic and pisolitic limestones, and beds of rubbly coral-rock. The *Upper Calcareous Grit* is found at Calne, where it contains the Calne Freestone, yielding abundant sea-urchins, but three miles farther north the Grit is represented by the Littlemore Clay Beds. Around Oxford there are two sub-divisions, an upper group of oolites, with associated reefs and shell banks (Coral Rag), resting on the Lower Calcareous Grit, mainly sand with limestone doggers. East of Wheatley both these divisions are replaced laterally almost entirely by a clay formation called the *Ampthill Clay*. The sands and limestones indicate shallow water conditions by the presence of false-bedding, ripple-marks, worm-burrows and fossil wood. The Ampthill Clay was laid down in deeper water and it replaces all the Corallian strata, except that around Arngrove Farm, about eight miles north-east of Oxford, where there is at the base some 6 ft. of chert. This is a porous, partly calcareous, partly sandy rock containing spicules of the sponge *Rhaxella* in great abundance, and it is named ' Arngrove Stone'. This rock, which also contains Lower Calcareous Grit fossils, is very distinctive and occurs as erratics in Drift gravels.

Kimmeridge Clay.—This formation (named from Kimmeridge in Dorset) is a dark clay, often shaly, with much selenite in places. Where the base is visible the Kimmeridge Clay may be seen to rest on an eroded surface of Corallian Beds. Fossils are abundant, the best preserved being in doggers. Locally the highest beds are sands or sandy clays and have been mistaken for the Portland Sand, but fossils show their real age. They are called Hartwell Clay, after a village near Aylesbury. The Kimmeridge Clay is much used for brick-making. At the top of the formation, beneath the Portland Beds, there is a marked stratigraphical break apparently extending all the way from North Wiltshire towards the Wash, and thence into Yorkshire. The marked variation in thickness (from 150 to 300 ft.) is due to the local absence of certain zones. At Kimmeridge 126 ft. of Kimmeridge Clay and 115 ft. of Portland Sands, missing in the London and Thames district, are present.

Portland Beds.—The Portland Beds (named from the Isle of Portland) consist in other districts of an upper limestone division and a lower sandy division; but it is now known that the latter is missing in Oxfordshire, the sandy top of the Kimmeridge Clay having been mistaken for it, and that there is an unconformity between the two formations. Portland Beds are found in patches only, as at Swindon, Bourton, Shotover Hill, Garsington, Great Milton, Brill, and Aylesbury. A little beyond the last-mentioned place the Lower Cretaceous rocks conceal them, if indeed they are present. They do not extend far under newer strata, however, for they are missing in a boring at Little Missenden. The Portland Beds are rubbly, creamy limestones overlaid locally by fine buff sands. They do not exceed 40 ft. in total thickness.

Purbeck Beds.—This, the highest division of the Jurassic System (named from the Isle of Purbeck), is seen in a few places only. A few feet of fossiliferous limestone and marl have been found at Swindon, Shotover Hill, Brill and elsewhere. They represent the estuarine and freshwater conditions which followed the close of the marine Jurassic period. At Swindon there is an unconformity between the Purbeck and Portland Beds, but in the Ayrlesbury district there seems to be a conformable succession. The Purbeck Beds are characterized by freshwater ostracods and occasional remains of wood, turtles, and insects.

Common fossils of the Middle and Upper Oolites include :—

KELLAWAYS BEDS.—Ammonites: *Cadoceras sublaeve; Sigaloceras calloviense.* Lamellibranchs: *Modiolus bipartitus; Gryphaea bilobata; Oxytoma inaequivalve.*

OXFORD CLAY.—Ammonites: *Kosmoceras prionae* ; *Cardioceras cardia.* Belemnite : *Cylindroteuthis puzosiana,* Lamellibranchs : *Ostrea* (*Liostrea*) *alimena*; *Grammatodon montaneyensis; Pleuromya recurva; Isognomon promytiloides.* Brachiopod : *Aulacothyris bernardina.*

CORALLIAN.—Ammonites : *Euaspidoceras catena*; *Perisphinctes plicatilis.* Lamellibranchs : *Trigonia hudlestoni; Lima* (*Plagiostoma*) *rigida.* Gastropods : *Pleurotomaria reticulata ; Natica murchisonae.* Brachiopod : *Rhynchonelloidea spathica.* Echinoid : *Hemicidaris intermedia.* Coral : *Isastraea explanata.*

KIMMERIDGE CLAY.—Ammonites : *Pectinatites pectinatus ; Pavlovia pallasoides.* Lamellibranchs : *Trigonia elongata ; Exogrya* (*Catinula*) *virgula ; Musculus autissidorensis ; Isognomon subplana ; Ostrea delta.*

PORTLAND BEDS.—Ammonite : *Kerberites okusensis.* Lamellibranchs : *Laevitrigonia gibbosa; Lucina portlandica.* Gastropods : *Aptyxiella portlandica; Natica ceres.*

PURBECK BEDS.—Lamellibranch : *Neomiodon* sp. Gastropod : *Viviparus cariniferus.* Ostracods : ' *Cypris* ' *purbeckensis ; Cypridea propunctata.*

IV. THE CRETACEOUS SYSTEM

WHERE both are fully represented the boundary between the Jurassic and Cretaceous Systems is one of convenience and does not indicate any great physical changes of conditons. The Purbeck Beds and the Wealden are, in fact, intimately connected.

The commonly unconformable junction between the Gault and the Lower Greensand, for instance in Wiltshire and Oxfordshire, has been taken as a dividing line between Upper and Lower Cretaceous, for descriptive purposes.

LOWER CRETACEOUS (WEALDEN AND LOWER GREENSAND)

Lower Cretaceous rocks occur in a narrow continuous outcrop that enters the district at Calne, in Wiltshire, and extends to Faringdon, in Berkshire. Beyond this place the rocks are found only in patches, widely separated, as far as Aylesbury, in Buckinghamshire. They appear again on the margin of the district, near Leighton Buzzard.

The formation dies out beneath the Upper Cretaceous in a comparatively short distance towards the south-east, as is proved by borings. It had been eroded before the unconformable Upper Cretaceous rocks were laid down.

The rocks are sands with subordinate bands of clay and are often known as ironsands on account of their highly ferruginous character. Frequently the sands are coarse and they often contain characteristically highly polished grains. In places they contain concretions known as box-stones (*i.e.* shells of ironstone containing a nucleus of sand). Small pebbles, including lydian stone, are sometimes found, especially near the base of the formation.

Only remnants of what was once an extensive sheet of Lower Cretaceous rocks now remain. In Oxfordshire and Buckinghamshire part of the strata, although in appearance similar to the rest, contain freshwater fossils, while the other masses when fossiliferous yield marine forms. The freshwater strata are conspicuous at Shotover Hill, near Oxford, whence the name *Shotover Sands*. There is a similar freshwater deposit at Brill, in Buckinghamshire. The fossils indicate that the rocks are the same age as some part of the Wealden Series of Sussex ; probably the Hastings Beds. These freshwater beds occur in a narrow belt extending south-eastward from Shotover to Great Haseley. The section at Great Haseley (Fig. 5, p. 17) shows the marked unconformity between the Wealden and the Portland Beds. The height of the section is about 22 ft.

The remainder of the Lower Cretaceous strata are presumably marine and to them the name Lower Greensand is best confined, but there are cases where the age is doubtful in the absence of fossils. These marine beds represent a transgression of the sea which no doubt washed away much of the earlier Shotover Sands.

At Faringdon there are deposits composed mainly of fragmentary sponges, bryozoa, mollusca, etc., with small pebbles of quartz, slate and hornstone. In places the gravel is cemented into a hard conglomerate. Faringdon is famous for its fossil calcareous sponges.

The Lower Cretaceous strata in this district do not as a rule exceed 50 ft. in thickness.

The following fossils may be mentioned as typical :—

WEALDEN.—Plant : *Cladophlebis sp.* Lamellibranchs : *Unio mantelli; Neomiodon sp.* Gastropod : *Viviparus elongatus.*

LOWER GREENSAND.—Cephalopod : *Anglonautilus undulatus.* Lamellibranchs : *Lopha diluviana; Exogyra sinuata; Toucasia lonsdalei.* Brachiopod: *Terebratella menardi.* Echinoids : *Cidaris farringdonensis; Peltastes wrighti.* Bryozoan : *Ceriopora polymorpha.* Sponges : *Raphidonema farringdonense; Peronidella ramosa.*

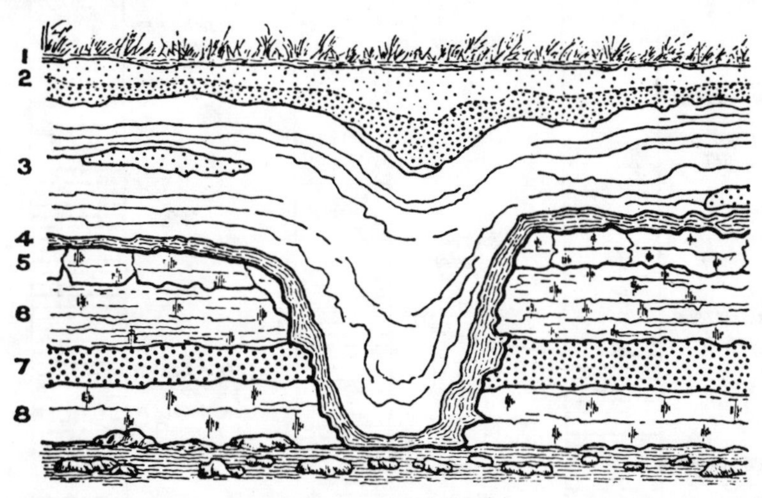

FIG. 5.—*Stone-pit at Great Haseley* (Fitton)

1. Soil		
2. Brown and red loam with fragments of ferruginous conglomerate, passing down into ferruginous sand	3 ft. to 6 ft. 0 in.	
3. Light grey firm clay or marl with plants, and lenses of reddish sand	6 ft. 6 in.	
4. Dark brown clay. At the bottom ferruginous sand alternates with the clay	1 ft. to 1 ft. 6 in.	
5, 6, 7, 8. Calcareous stone-beds and sands (Portland) . about	11 ft. 0 in.	

UPPER CRETACEOUS

Deposits of the Chalk sea mark a widespread stratigraphical base, but Gault and Upper Greensand are here described with Upper Cretaceous.

Gault and Upper Greensand.—The Upper Greensand was originally called simply ' The Greensand,' but later, sandy beds below the Gault were confused with it and so an Upper and a Lower Greensand separated by the Gault clay came to be distinguished. It is now known that the Upper Greensand is the sandy equivalent of part of the Gault formation, formed in shallow water, whilst the Gault clay was formed farther out to sea. Sometimes one, sometimes the other, fails, or, as is often the case, there may be some Gault clay covered by Upper Greensand as the water shallowed. Consequently it becomes necessary to regard the two as one formation and the name Selbornian (from Selborne, Hants) was suggested by Jukes-Browne for the combined Gault and Upper Greensand, but this name has not been accepted. There are in fact three facies, greensand, malmstone and gault clay (Fig. 6, p. 18). Greensand owes its colour

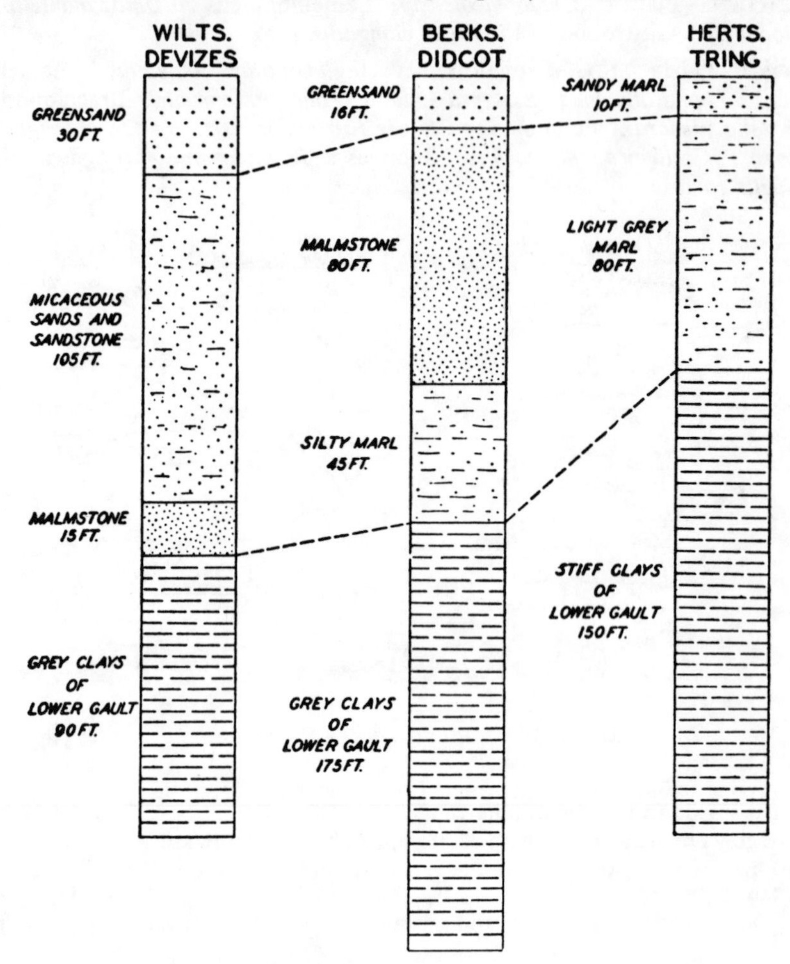

FIG. 6.—*Comparative Vertical Sections through the Gault and Upper Greensand* (after A. J. Jukes-Browne)

to the presence of dark green grains of fresh glauconite, but sometimes it is stained with ochreous tints after the glauconite has been weathered. Malmstone, malm or firestone is a pale rock consisting of sponge spicules and colloidal (uncrystallized) silica, usually up to about 40 per cent., with clay, calcareous matter, and some mica. It resembles a fine-grained sandstone and has been used as a building stone at Potterne, near Devizes. The name 'firestone' indicates that it was formerly in demand for lining kilns and glass-furnaces. The term 'malm' is also used commercially for a brickmaking clay, which is quite a different material. Gault is a local word used for a stiff blue clay, but the geologist uses it as the name of a definite formation. Near Calne much of the

Gault consists of yellow, grey, or lilac-tinted, silty, micaceous clays and marly clays.

Where the Gault cuts out part of the Lower Greensand there are no strata to represent the considerable interval of time that elapsed between these formations. To the Chalk above, however, there is frequently a perfect transition, especially where the Upper Greensand is replaced by Gault. The Lower Greensand having filled up depressions, the Gault base itself is fairly flat.

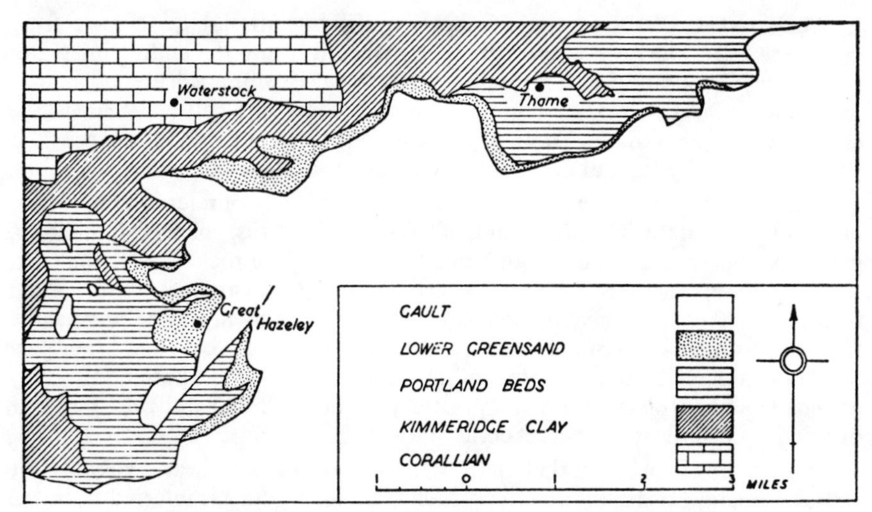

FIG. 7.—*Map showing the overlap of the Gault near Thame*

The Gault resting successively on Lower Greensand, Portland Beds and Kimmeridge Clay near Thame is shown in Fig. 7 (p. 19).

The probable position of land and sea at the time when the Gault and Upper Greensand were being laid down is shown in Fig. 8 (p. 21). The stippling indicates the area over which the formations probably extended but from which they have been subsequently denuded.

Near Calne, in Wiltshire, the thickness of the formation is about 160 ft., made up of greensand and malmstone. In Berkshire the malmstone is developed to a local maximum of 90 ft. and continues through Oxfordshire, becoming thinner until it entirely disappears in Buckinghamshire, where it is replaced by Gault. Above the malmstone there is about 12 ft. of soft greensand in Oxfordshire, and the combined Gault and Upper Greensand is about 284 ft. At Tring, in Hertfordshire, the greensand has become 6 ft. of greenish silt and the formation is about 236 ft. in all.

When regard is paid to fossils rather than to lithology the formation is divisible into Lower and Upper Gault, the latter including the malmstone and greensand.

Phosphatic nodules have been worked at two horizons; the lower one being from 20 to 30 ft. above the base of the Gault and, at Towersey, near Thame, 3 or 4 in. thick, the nodules lying in a stiff marl. The upper horizon is about 150 ft. from the base of the Gault and the nodules occur in a seam of greensand which is regarded as the base of the Upper Gault. The presence of the nodules and the differences between the fossils of the Lower and Upper Gault indicate a gap in time and some erosion between the two divisions.

A few fossils characteristic of this area are :—

GAULT.—Ammonites: *Mortoniceras inflatum; Hoplites dentatus.* Belemnite: *Neohibolites minimus.* Lamellibranchs: *Inoceramus sulcatus; I. concentricus.*

UPPER GREENSAND.—Lamellibranchs : *Entolium orbiculare ; Aucellina gryphaeoides.*

Chalk.—The Chalk formation shows a striking lithological change from bottom to top. The lowest layers grade imperceptibly into the underlying Gault or Upper Greensand, but, ascending in the succession, calcareous matter gradually replaces clay or sand until the rock becomes the soft white limestone called chalk. This differs from other limestones in appearance because it is porous and earthy instead of having a compact crystalline character.

It is often stated that chalk is made up almost entirely of microscopic fossils, but this is inaccurate. The proportion of microscopic fossils, chiefly foraminifera, varies, but never forms more than 5 to 10 per cent. of the rock. By far the most abundant constituent is, however, exceedingly fine calcareous matter which forms from 40 to 90 per cent of the whole. This is probably produced organically from the disintegration of planktonic algae. In the Lower Chalk and lower part of the Middle Chalk fragments of shells, especially *Inoceramus*, are very abundant and in places form the greater part of the rock, but they decrease in amount upwards in the succession.

It is no longer believed that chalk was formed in a deep sea. Probably the shores were not far distant and deposition in shallow water is inferred from the nodular hard bands, the Totternhoe Stone, Melbourn Rock and Chalk Rock, and the fossils they contain. These indicate a rising of the sea-floor, and it is very difficult to suppose that the water was very deep in between the shallow water periods. Recently it has been suggested by Sir Edward Bailey that a pure limestone, like chalk, might be deposited near the shore line if, owing to a desert climate, there were no rivers to bring down detritus. The small quantity of detrital material present is very varied and also indicates derivation from a continental rather than a volcanic source. The boulders and smaller fragments of granite and other rocks that have been found occasionally in chalk appear to have been floated from shore either by ice or attached to tree-roots.

Chalk usually shows little sign of bedding other than by lines of flints in the upper part.

The prominent escarpment made by the Chalk is illustrated in Fig. 9 (p. 22) and also in Fig. 10 (p. 24). The former shows how the Upper Greensand is frequently hidden by downwash from the face of the escarpment.

The higher part of the Chalk contains flints, rarely in the Middle, but abundantly in the Upper Chalk. Flint consists of an intimate mixture of soluble and insoluble silica. It is believed by some geologists that it was formed by the solution of fossils with siliceous skeletons, such as sponges, contained in the Chalk; but other authorities consider that the greater part is of inorganic origin and was deposited from sea-water in colloidal masses (*gels*) on the sea-floor during the formation of the Chalk. Flints occur either as irregular masses, in definite layers, or as isolated nodules scattered through the rock ; or as thin tabular layers filling cracks, whether vertical, horizontal or oblique.

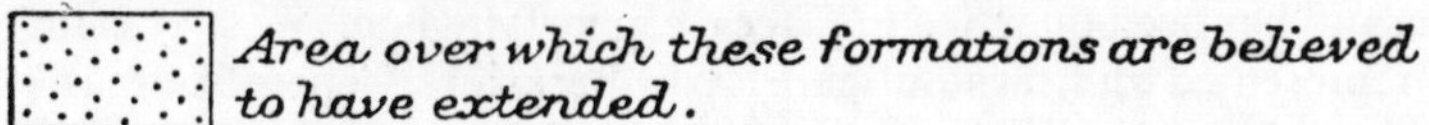

FIG. 8.—*Map to show extent of the Gault and Upper Greensand*
(A. J. Jukes-Browne)

Heavy ball-like lumps are sometimes found, especially in the Lower Chalk. When broken open they show a radial mass of brassy material which is the mineral marcasite (iron sulphide, FeS_2). On the surface the mineral is weathered to brown hydrated oxide of iron. The rusty-brown stains sometimes seen in chalk are due to the same cause : the oxidation of marcasite.

The Chalk is divided into :—

Upper Chalk = Chalk with Flints

Middle Chalk }
Lower Chalk } = Chalk without Flints

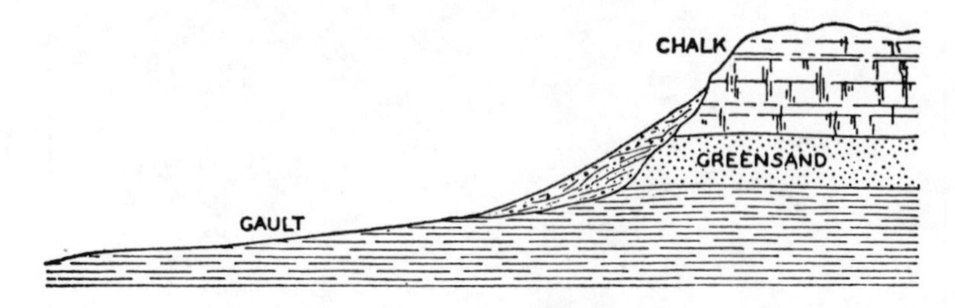

FIG. 9.—*A frequent aspect of the chalk escarpment in N. Wiltshire* (A. J. Jukes-Browne)

The section (Fig. 10, p. 24) taken through the Chalk escarpment at Coombe Hill, Wendover, shows the relation of the shape of the ground to the divisions of the Chalk. The hard Chalk Rock and Melbourn Rock hold up the soft intervening chalk and this is aided by the prosity of the latter, which absorbs the rain. The lower beds, which are soft, contain some clay, and hold up water, form the plain in front of the Chiltern Hills. The section also shows the slight dip of the strata. The top of the hills is covered by the superficial deposit called the Clay-with-flints (p. 43. *See also* Fig. 18, p. 48).

Lower Chalk.—Usually the Chalk commences with a soft glauconitic marl (known as the Chloritic Marl, owing to the former misidentification of the glauconite in the marl as the green mineral chlorite) making a gradual passage from the underlying Upper Greensand. The *Chalk Marl*, which follows, is a highly calcareous clay, somewhat resembling Gault. About 50 or 60 ft. above the base there is, locally, a bed of very compact chalk named the *Marl Rock* and traceable by a line of strong springs. At the top of the Chalk Marl comes a similar hard bed, the *Totternhoe Stone* (named after Totternhoe in Bedfordshire), resting on what is practically normal chalk although included in the Chalk Marl. The stone is largely made up of minute fragments of the shell *Inoceramus* which give it a grey tint and gritty feel, together with greater hardness than ordinary chalk, for which it can nevertheless be mistaken when wet. Although best developed in Bedfordshire and Cambridgeshire, the Totternhoe Stone occurs in our area and has been quarried in places, *e.g.* at Ivinghoe. West of Ivinghoe it is poorly represented and dies out entirely in Berkshire. There is occasionally in Buckinghamshire a similar bed situated 30 to 35 ft. above the Totternhoe Stone. The remainder of the Lower Chalk is ordinary chalk without flints, except that in North Wiltshire and Berkshire there are masses of whitish siliceous chalk largely made of sponge fragments and forming incipient flints. At the top of the Lower Chalk is the Belemnite Marl—a shaly marl about 2 ft. thick and usually containing a thin bed of hard chalk in the middle. The Lower Chalk forms, on the whole flattish land below the escarpment of the higher beds and is in many places covered by superficial deposits.

In North Wiltshire and Berkshire the formation is about 240 ft. thick. In Oxfordshire it is nearer 200 ft. of which the Chalk Marl forms about 120 ft. In

Buckinghamshire the Chalk Marl is not over 100 ft. and the whole of the Lower Chalk probably does not exceed 180 ft. In Essex the Lower Chalk and the greater part of the Middle Chalk do not appear at the surface but are known in borings. Similarly, in the parts of Hampshire and Surrey falling into our district the Lower and Middle Chalk have been reached in borings. In Hampshire the Lower Chalk may be about 170 ft. and in Surrey about 220 ft. thick in the sections of those counties with which we are concerned.

A few fossils characteristic of the Lower Chalk are mentioned below. In the normal chalk ammonites are almost confined to the hard beds, such as the Melbourn Rock of the Middle Chalk, but in the Chalk Marl they are more abundant :—

Ammonites : *Mantelliceras mantelli ; Schloenbachia varians.* Belemnite : *Actinocamax plenus* (in Belemnite Marl). Lamellibranchs: *Inoceramus crippsi ; Plicatula inflata ; Ostrea vesicularis.* Sponge : *Stauronema carteri.*

Middle Chalk.—This division commences with the Melbourn Rock (named after Melbourn in Cambridgeshire), a hard creamy chalk, often nodular and generally from 8 to 10 ft. thick. The softness of the Belemnite Marl below helps it to form a shelf on the main Chalk escarpment.

West of Swindon the Middle Chalk is about 140 to 150 ft. thick, and in Berkshire about 150 ft. In Oxfordshire it increases to 200 ft., and in Buckinghamshire it varies between 200 and 220 ft. The thickness in the part of Surrey included in our district is probably somewhat less.

The Melbourn Rock is the best stratum for fossils, including ammonites, but fossils in general are not common in the Middle Chalk. The following may be mentioned :—

Ammonite : *Lewesiceras peramplum.* Lamellibranch : *Inoceramus labiatus.* Brachiopods : *Terebratulina lata ; Orbirhynchia cuvieri.* Echinoid : *Conulus subrotundus.*

Upper Chalk.—The Upper Chalk is on the whole softer than the Middle Chalk and in it flints are abundant as a rule. The base of the division is a hard band called the *Chalk Rock*, which in the area north of the Thames is the most prominent horizon in the Chalk. It consists of one or more beds of hard, creamy limestone each about 1 ft. thick, usually with scattered green grains of glauconite. Between the creamy limestone bands are layers of hard nodular chalk in a softer matrix. The nodules are frequently slightly phosphatic. Ammonites and gastropods occur, amongst other fossils, especially in the nodular layers. In parts of Oxfordshire and Buckinghamshire there is a hard band about 14 to 20 ft. above the Chalk Rock, for which it may easily be mistaken.

In North Wiltshire the Upper Chalk is about 300 ft. thick, and it is about 337 ft. in Berkshire. At Taplow, Buckinghamshire, it is about 330 ft. thick, but it is less over the Chiltern plateau. Near Tring there may be about 230 ft. A great deal of Upper Chalk is missing owing to denudation before the Eocene rocks were deposited. There is little difference between the dips of the Chalk and the Eocene beds, but, if followed down the dip-slope, borings through the Eocene show a thickening of the Chalk in that direction. There is, in fact, a great gap in time between Chalk and Eocene not represented by strata in this

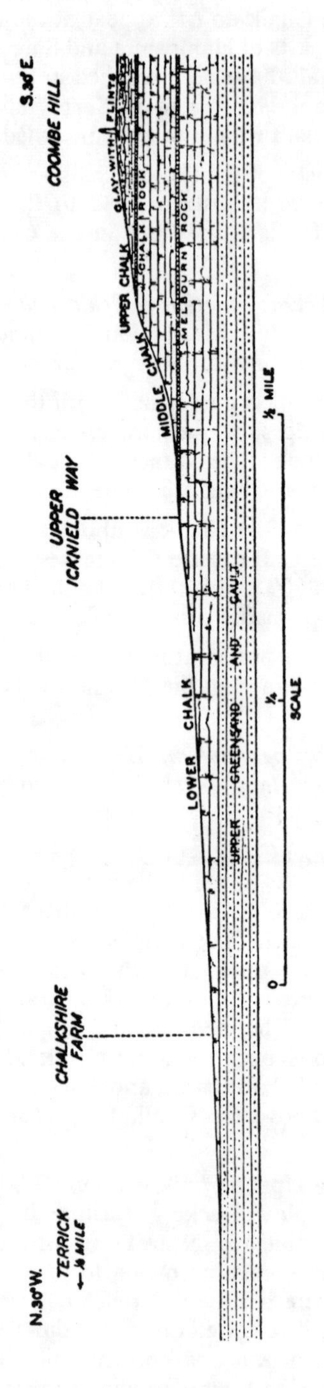

FIG. 10.—*Section through the Chalk Escarpment near Wendover*

district. In a boring at Harwich, in Essex, the thickness of the Chalk (all divisions) was 890 ft.

A small area of Upper Chalk in Surrey and Kent falls into our district. Near the base in these counties are beds of tough, thick-bedded chalk with hard yellow nodules, and in some places a powdery chalk with many lumps surrounded by greenish films. The films are striated as if by slickensiding. The thickness of the Upper Chalk is here about 320 ft. and the uppermost layers are shown by the fossils to be approximately of the same age as those at Taplow, the highest chalk in the Chiltern Hills.

In this southern area the overstep of the Eocene is more marked than on the northern crop and some of the Eocene outliers rest unevenly on low horizons of the Upper Chalk.

Although fossils are abundant in the Upper Chalk, they are very unequally spaced and in many chalk-pits are difficult to find. They are most readily seen after the frosts of winter have scaled off adhering chalk, when they often project from the rock-surface. The commonest fossils are sea-urchins, which are accompanied by sponges, lamellibranchs and brachiopods. Less abundant are corals, crinoids, starfish, polyzoans, and fishes. The hard, creamy limestones of the Chalk Rock in the Chiltern hills are not very fossiliferous but sometimes yield perfect specimens of Rhynchonellidae and less frequently a coral. A few of the commoner fossils are listed below :—

Fish : *Lamna appendiculata.* Ammonoids : *Hyphantoceras reussianum ; Scaphites geinitzi.* Lamellibranchs : *Ostrea vesicularis ; Lima (Plagiostoma) hoperi ; Spondylus spinosus ; Inoceramus lamarcki ; Chlamys cretosus ; Neithea quinquecostata.* Gastropods : *Bathrotomaria perspectiva ; 'Turbo' geinitzi.* Brachiopods : *Crania egnabergensis ; Orbirhynchia reedensis ; Gibbithyris semiglobosa ; Terebratulina striatula ; Kingena lima.* Echinoids : *Holaster placenta ; Conulus albogalerus ; Micraster praecursor ; M. coranguinum ; M. cortestudinarium ; Echinocorys scutata ; Stereocidaris sceptifera ; Tylocidaris clavigera.* Crinoids : *Marsupites testudinarius ; Bourgueticrinus ellipticus.* Sponge : *Porosphaera globularis.*

V. EOCENE

According to some geologists the Eocene strata are not of sufficient importance to be classified as a System, but they are united with the succeeding Oligocene strata to form the Palaeogene System. Similarly, the newer formations, Miocene, Pliocene and Pleistocene, are by some regarded as together forming the Neogene System. In the London and Thames region the Oligocene and Miocene divisions of the Tertiary Era are missing.

The Eocene strata comprise the following formations :—

Barton Beds		Upper Bagshot
Bracklesham Beds	=	Middle Bagshot
Bagshot Beds		Lower Bagshot

London Clay and Claygate Beds
Woolwich and Reading, and Blackheath Beds
Thanet Beds

Until recently the highest three of the above formations were grouped together as Upper, Middle, and Lower Bagshot Beds. It is, however, now recognized that the Bagshot Series of the Thames Basin can be subdivided into the three divisions long known in Hampshire, namely, the Barton, Bracklesham, and Bagshot Beds.

The great interval of time between the deposition of the Chalk and that of the Eocene strata in the Thames district is indicated by the sudden change in lithology and by the Eocene rocks frequently resting on a chalk surface bored by molluscs. The ordinary piping of Eocene into Chalk so often seen is, however, misleading, as it is to a considerable extent not original but due to percolation and solution of chalk by water at a much later date. When exposed at some distance within the margin of the Tertiary rocks, in artificial exposures the junction is sharp and level.

As a rule the Eocene contains at its base angular flints covered with a greenish or blackish coat and embedded in dark clay or loam. When the Thanet Beds are absent this layer, the 'Bull Head Bed,' occurs beneath the Woolwich and Reading Beds. Of actual discordance of dip between Eocene and Chalk there is little appearance, for both formations have very gentle dips. Nevertheless, when the Chalk is zoned by fossils over a considerable area it is found that the Eocene rests on different zones in different places, showing that there is a real discordance between the two formations. The relationship of the Eocene to the Chalk is illustrated by Fig. 11 (p. 27), a section drawn through the Windsor dome. The Chalk is thinnest at the crest of the dome and thickest in synclinal troughs on either side. This is due to erosion of the Chalk before the Eocene was deposited. The final uplift occurred after the Eocene was laid down.

Thanet Beds.—This, the lowest division of the Eocene, is found only in the eastern part of the district. It appears in a narrow outcrop along the margin of the Chalk, extending as far west as East Clandon, Surrey. Traced by borings, it is found to terminate towards the north-east along a line drawn through Weybridge, Sunbury, Ealing, and Hendon. In Essex it extends underground

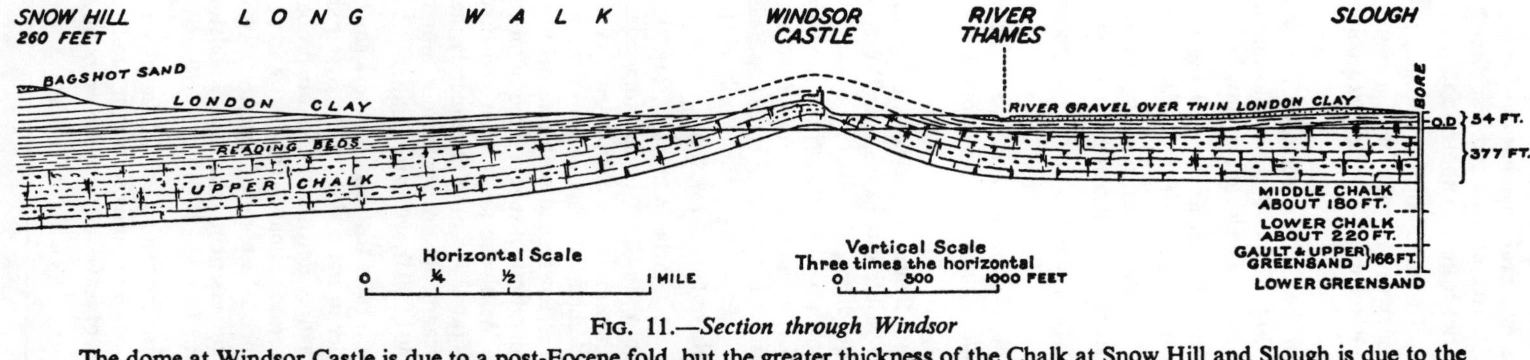

FIG. 11.—*Section through Windsor*

The dome at Windsor Castle is due to a post-Eocene fold, but the greater thickness of the Chalk at Snow Hill and Slough is due to the unconformity between the Eocene and the Chalk

northward to a point beyond Braintree, but outside this line the Woolwich and Reading Beds overlap the Thanet Beds and rest directly on Chalk. The thickness of the formation varies from 0 to about 75 ft.

The Thanet Beds consist mainly of fine-grained, pale yellow or grey sand, passing downward into silt, with, at the base, a layer of green loam with the green-coated flints already mentioned. The green colour is due to the mineral glauconite.

The eroded surface of the Chalk covered by Thanet Beds was formerly well exposed at Chislehurst (Fig. 12, p. 29). The old mining galleries in chalk are known as ' Chislehurst Caves '. The locality is now for the greater part built over.

The supposed position of land and sea at the time of formation of the Thanet Beds has been worked out by Prof. S. W. Wooldridge, Fig. 14 (p. 32).

Thanet sand is used extensively for moulding (which may have determined the site of Woolwich Arsenal) and in places for building and glass sands.

The fossils are all marine, and about seventy species are known, including the following :—

Lamellibranchs : *Pholadomya konincki ; Arctica morrisi ; Nemocardium semigranulatum ; Corbula regulbiensis.* Gastropod : *Aporrhais sowerbyi.*

Woolwich and Reading Beds.—These beds occur in three facies. In East Kent they are marine fossiliferous sands. In West Kent, East Surrey, and Essex they are estuarine deposits called Woolwich Beds, which give place towards the west and north to fluviatile strata known as Reading Beds. The loams of the Woolwich Beds pass laterally into Reading Beds without a distinct line of division. In the intermediate area estuarine beds occur below fluviatile strata. In West Kent and East Surrey the Woolwich Beds are overlain by the Blackheath Beds which do not extend west of Croydon.

The Woolwich Beds are a variable series of clays, loams, sands, and pebble beds, locally cemented into sandstone or conglomerate. The sands are yellow, greenish, or brown, containing layers of mottled clay and sometimes bands of lignite. Shells are found chiefly in clay at about the middle of the formation. The ' Bottom Bed ' is a greenish sand with flint-pebbles where Thanet Sand is present below, but unworn flints if it rest directly on the Chalk. This bottom Bed persists beyond the Woolwich facies area and occurs below the fluviatile Reading Beds, at least as far as Reading. Frequently the chalk beneath is bored by animals, and shell fragments are sometimes found in the burrows. The thickness is from about 40 to 90 ft. with an average of about 70 ft.

A bed containing freshwater fossils occurs in a small area between Leytonstone and Croydon, either in the middle of the oyster shell-bed or replacing it. Leaf-bearing beds at Croydon, Lewisham, etc., are probably of the same age and contain remains of vertebrate animals. The freshwater horizon was represented in the Rotherhithe Tunnel by a band of limestone associated with green marl (Fig. 13, p. 30). This impersistent calcareous mudstone was unfossiliferous, but elsewhere it contains *Viviparus*, *Unio*, *Pitharella* and other freshwater shells.

The Reading Beds are the widest-spread facies. They consist of mottled, plastic clays, and light-coloured sands with thin bands of flint pebbles. Fossils are rare, but impressions of leaves are sometimes found.

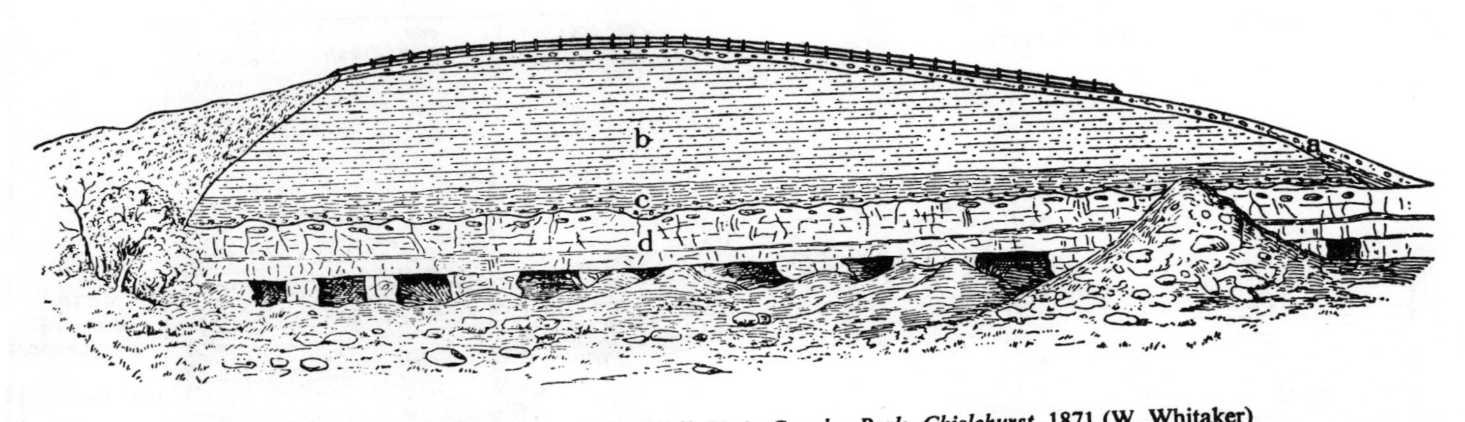

FIG. 12.—*Diagrammatic Section of the Chalk Pit in Camden Park, Chislehurst*, 1871 (W. Whitaker)

a=Loamy and gravelly soil.

Thanet Sand { *b*=Clayey bedded sand, somewhat darker than usual, about 30 ft.
c=Basement-bed, 5½ ft., clayey greenish and with green-coated flints ; the lower half very dark. Many very small pipes in the chalk.

d=Chalk with flints ; dip about 1° N.W. along the face. A somewhat hard bed, about 40 in. thick, 7 to 8 ft. down, forms the roof of the galleries. The bed next below has a hard top.

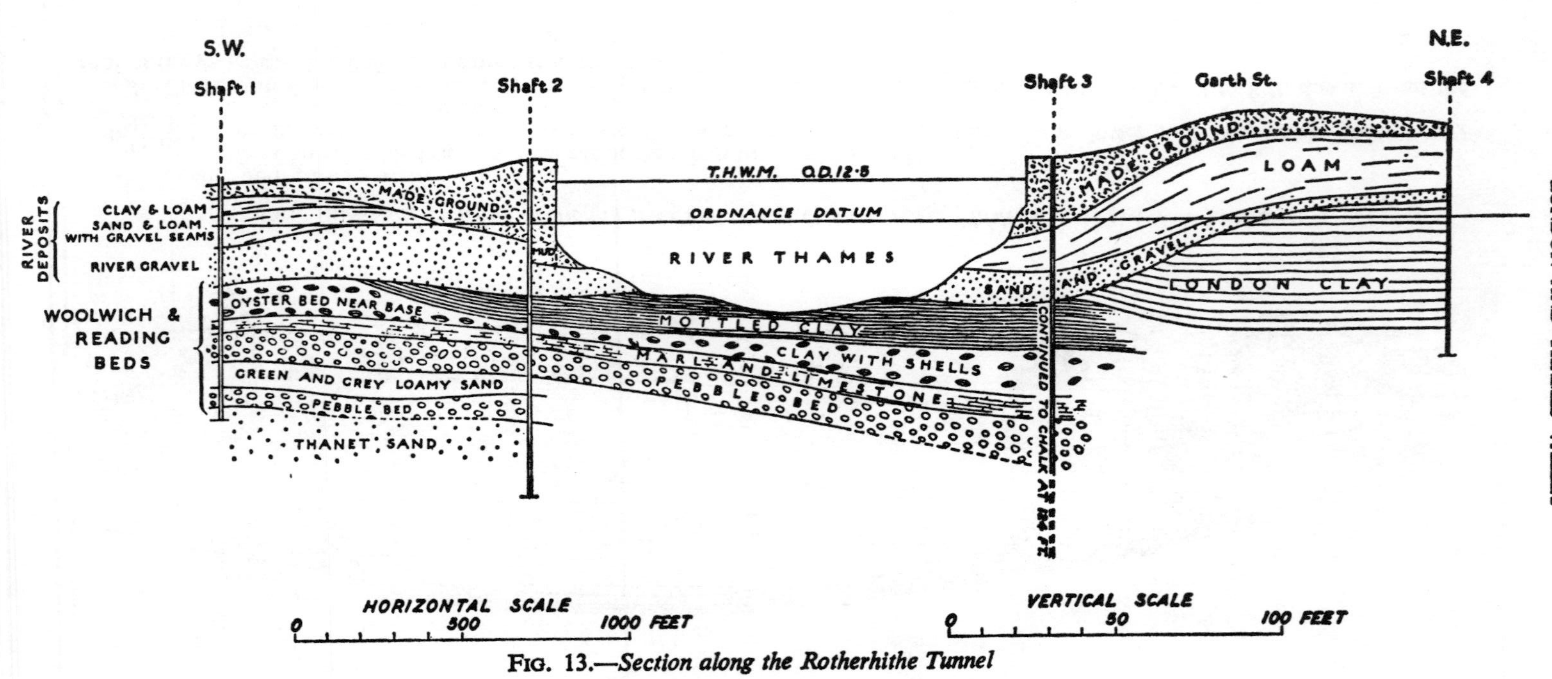

FIG. 13.—*Section along the Rotherhithe Tunnel*

In the west of the district, in Savernake Forest, the Reading Beds are reduced to about 15 ft. of plastic clay. They thicken eastward and near Reading comprise about 30 to 50 ft. of clay overlying 20 to 40 ft. of sand, in all about 70 to 90 ft. From the rim of the London Basin the thickness increases towards the middle, reaching a maximum of about 90 ft., as at Southall. East of the River Colne the whole formation becomes sandy with subordinate clay. This however, is a local condition and at Ruislip sand comprises about 4 ft. out of 57 ft. of strata.

Sarsens, or ' greywethers,' are boulders scattered about the area and are in many cases derived from the Reading Beds. They represent parts of the sand that have been cemented into hard shapeless masses by percolating waters. When the matrix has been removed by weathering they are left behind and may be carried by ice as boulders. The pebble-beds, similarly cemented, form lumps of conglomerate called the Hertfordshire Puddingstone. Varieties are known as when the flints are only sub-rounded, or when the conglomerate passes into a sarsen. Other Eocene sand formations, for example the Bagshot Beds, may also produce sarsens.

At Lane End, west of High Wycombe, the Reading Beds consist of sand, loamy above, and irregular beds of gravel. These contain abundant small vein-quartz pebbles and subangular flints, in addition to the usual flint-pebbles. Individual strata are irregular and cut out one another. Clay bands are found, but for the most part are grey instead of the usual mottled red colour, and the clay is often in lumps. The deposits are unlike normal Reading Beds, but fortunately their age is proved by the presence of London Clay above them.

There are a good many outliers in the Chiltern region and when sections are visible the strata are seen to be disturbed. This may be due in part to the effect of ice and snow in incoherent materials, but the Lane End sections show that in some cases it is an original structure of the rock.

In Fig. 14 (p. 32), following Prof. S. W. Wooldridge, the position of land and water is shown at three stages of Lower Eocene time, the broken lines indicating the approximate positions of rivers. In the top map the position of the coast line in Thanet Sand Time is shown, whilst the middle figure shows the position in early Woolwich and Reading times. It will be noticed that the sea had spread beyond the limits of the Thanet Sand sea. The lowest figure shows that in later Woolwich and Reading times the sea retreated considerably, leaving a lagoon of brackish water between land and sea.

Characteristic fossils of the Woolwich and Reading Beds are :—

WOOLWICH BEDS (ESTUARINE).—Lamellibranchs : *Ostrea bellovacina ; Glycymeris plumstediensis ; Corbicula cordata.* Gastropods : *Brotia melanioides ; Tympanotonus funatus.*

WOOLWICH BEDS (FRESHWATER BED).—Lamellibranch : *Unio subparallela.* Gastropods : *Viviparus lentus ; Stenothyra parkinsoni.*

READING BEDS.—Plants : *Aneimia subcretacea ; Laurus ; Acer.*

BLACKHEATH BEDS.—This division consists of pebble-beds and sands, the pebbles being almost exclusively well-rounded flints and the sand of quartz with flint chips. Very rarely a flat pebble of sarsen (' penny stone ') is found and sometimes a pebble-bed is seen to be cemented into a conglomerate. The Blackheath Beds rest irregularly on Woolwich Beds, locally cutting well into them, and near Caterham and Worms Heath they overlap them and rest in

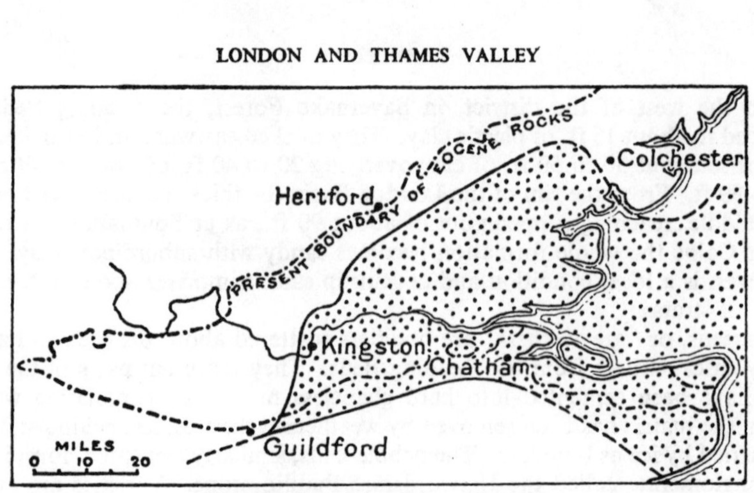

THANET SANDS TIMES.

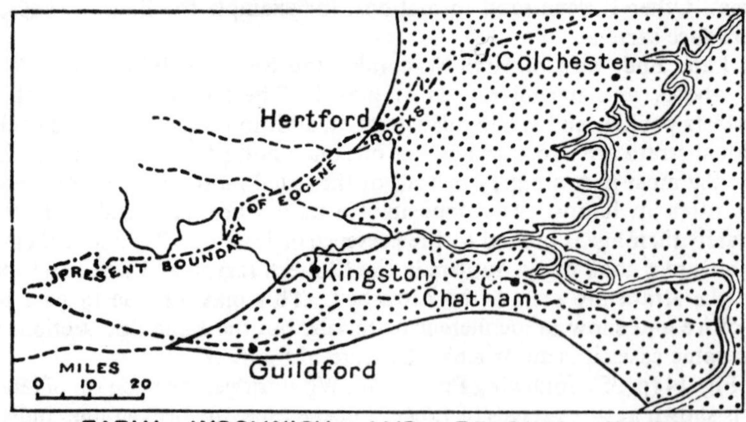

EARLY WOOLWICH AND READING TIMES.

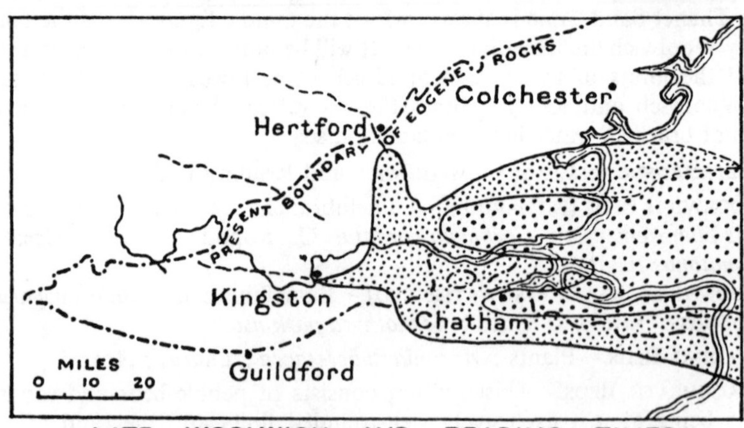

LATE WOOLWICH AND READING TIMES.

FIG. 14.—*Distribution of land and water in Lower Eocene times* (after S. W. Wooldridge)

contact with Chalk. Fossils when present may be marine, estuarine, or fresh-water shells and are intermediate in character between Woolwich Beds and London Clay forms. In a few places fossils are numerous.

The Blackheath Beds extend westward as far as a curved line from Lewisham and Beckenham to Croydon, where they are well exposed at Croham Hurst. Their thickness is from 0 to about 40 ft. They are a local accumulation of shingle and sand derived, no doubt, in part from pre-existing pebble-beds.

The fossils include :—

Lamellibranchs : *Glycymeris plumstediensis ; Corbicula* (*Tellinocyclas*) *tellinoides ; Dosiniopsis bellovacina.* Gastropods : *Sigatica abducta ; Euspira glaucinoides.*

London Clay.—The greater part of the London Clay is a stiff, dark or bluish-grey clay which weathers at outcrop to brown. Characteristic of the London Clay are the septaria, or concretions of argillaceous limestone, occurring as layers of nodules and, in some cases, containing numerous fossils. They are known as cement stones, as they were at one time in great demand for making cement. The lowest part of the formation is a sandy bed with black flint-pebbles and occasional layers of sandstone and is known as the Basement Bed. In the vicinity of London the London Clay passes up into the more sandy Claygate Beds, but in other places these are missing and the London Clay is covered abruptly by the Bagshot Sand. It is probable that the oxidation of iron pyrites, present in the bluish clay, resulting in the formation of sulphuric acid which attacks the calcareous shells and nodules and forms crystals of gypsum (selenite), is responsible for the absence of London Clay fossils in most localities.

As here defined, with the Claygate Beds separated, the London Clay reaches a maximum of about 430 ft. at Wimbledon, Esher, and Brentwood. On the north side of the London Basin it is about 350 ft. thick at Highgate. In the middle of the Basin a great deal had been denuded, so that in Tottenham Court Road there is only about 63 ft. and in the City from 85 to 130 ft.

The following are a few of the commoner fossils :—

Cephalopod : *Cimomia imperialis.* Lamellibranchs : *Nemocardium nitens ; Arctica morrisi ; Glycymeris brevirostris ; Panopea intermedia.* Gastropods : *Aporrhais sowerbyi ; Athleta* (*Volutospina*) *nodosa ; Hippochrenes amplus ; Xenophora extensa.* Annelid : *Ditrupa plana.*

The London Clay contains numerous plant remains, and many hundreds of specimens, belonging to over 50 plant families, have been collected from various localities in the Thames Valley, particularly from the foreshore of the Isle of Sheppey, just outside the present area.

At Sheppey large blocks of fossil wood are common, but the great majority of the plant fossils are fruits and seeds. Very few records exist, however, of these fruits and seeds having been found in the clay mass of the cliffs ; this is to be expected, since they probably occur but sparsely, and generally have the same colour as the clay. The sorting action of the waves, however, acting on fallen masses of clay, collects the fossil seeds into pockets on the beach.

These plant remains have attracted attention for more than 200 years, and as early as 1757 a number of drawings of seeds and other objects were made. In 1810 a catalogue of fossil fruits and seeds from Sheppey was made by Francis Crow, of Faversham, " the Result of upwards of Twenty Years Collecting ".

This catalogue contains 831 drawings ; unfortunately, the great majority of the objects represented by the drawings cannot be identified, probably because, as Crow states, " the person that figured them was never learned to draw ".

In the Geological Museum is a large oil painting by Mr. E. Marsden Wilson, here reproduced from a photograph as Plate II, showing an imaginary scene in the south-east of England at a date something like fifty million years ago, when the London Clay was being deposited as sediment. At that time the district was under the sea, for the whole area is either covered, or has been covered, by London Clay and this was deposited in the sea. The coast, however, was not far away and was probably low-lying, for there were no hard rocks exposed to make high ground. The character of the animals and plants found fossil, considered together, throws light on the geographical conditions and it is supposed that the site of the district was near the estuary of a large river. The probability that the water was salt is shown by the presence of shells of marine type found in the clay, but the proximity of the coast and of a river is shown by the presence of crocodiles.

The climate under which any specific deposit was accumulated may often be deduced from a study of a contained fossil flora, provided a sufficient number of genera have been discovered. The London Clay has in fact yielded, in particular to Mrs. E. M. Reid and Miss M. E. J. Chandler, an ample flora, from the study of which they support the theory that the contemporary climate was that of a tropical rain-forest—a conclusion stated in their comprehensive description of the London Clay Flora published in 1933 by the Trustees of the British Museum (Natural History).

These authors point out that in H. N. Moseley's *Notes by a Naturalist on the " Challenger,"* published in 1892, a description of the detritus of the Ambernoh River of New Guinea reads as if it were the authentic record of conditions that had existed in the London Clay sea of the Sheppey district. Moseley says that various fruits and seeds, and other plant fragments, were abundant in the water, floating in the midst of small aggregations of floating timber. Among them were the seeds of littoral plants but in addition there were seeds of 40 to 50 inland species. Very small seeds were as abundant as large ones. Leaves were generally absent, having been sorted out, and deposited in the mud nearer the shore. This observation explains the absence of leaves among the numerous other plant remains at Sheppey.

One of the most striking plants found fossil in the London Clay is a palm very much like the *Nipa* palm that now grows abundantly in the Sunderbunds, at the mouth of the Ganges, in India. The plant was described by Sir J. Hooker as a low, stemless palm, with pale yellow-green tufts of feathery leaves, bearing at the base of the leaves a great head of nuts. The fruits are about a foot in diameter and made up of closely packed seeds, each as large as a hen's egg, and these ripen in early winter. In Plate II a large mass of Nipa palm is seen above and to the right of the crocodiles. As the picture depicts a summer scene the fruits could not be shown. The seeds float on the water to considerable distances and germinate in the mud, and a number of them are shown near the Nipa on the brackish water, to the left of the crocodiles. There were also mangroves in the swamp.

Another interesting plant is the *Sabal* palm. At the present time this grows in damp places and the fossil representatives are assumed to have had a similar

PLATE II

IDEAL LANDSCAPE OF THE LONDON CLAY PERIOD

(For detailed explanation see pp. 34–35)

(MN 1911)

PLATE III (A 1075)

Sarsens in Clay-with-flints, Walter's Ash, Bucks.

PLATE IV

Valley Gravel
in the
Wendover Gap

(A 1401)

PLATE V

Deep Channel at Steps Hill, Ivinghoe, looking up the valley

(A 2500)

habitat. The base of the trunk ends in a knob surrounded by a dense mass of contorted roots. Laurels and Acacia-like plants were common, while among the climbing plants were numerous vines.

In the illustration, the ground to the left of the Sabal palms is sandy and at the bottom of the picture on the left side is a tangled mass of ferns. It is not known with certainty if grass existed in London Clay time and so the ferns, which are known to have lived then, have been shown covering the ground instead of grass. The tree in flower is a *Magnolia*, which now grows in Britain.

The animals shown differ markedly from living types. The mammals (' animals ' of everyday language) are of great interest because they show characters not now found together in the same animal. Primitive mammals are known to have existed as long ago as the Triassic period, but it was not until the giant reptiles had died out at the end of the Cretaceous period that mammals became the dominant land animals. Released from the danger of the carnivorous reptiles, they underwent rapid development. At the time of the formation of the London Clay some of the mammals had already developed a good deal from the most primitive types, but they were nevertheless very odd-looking creatures from a present-day point of view.

In the middle of the picture are three specimens of *Coryphodon*, which resembled in build and sometimes in size a hippopotamus. Those in the picture are about the size of a cow. The feet were shaped something like an elephant's and there were five toes on each foot. The Coryphodon had strong canine teeth to protect it from enemies and was an omnivorous feeder. The group of ungulates (hoofed mammals) to which it belongs, the Amblypoda, has no living descendants, but for a time it was the most prominent group of ungulates.

Hyracotherium, an animal about the size of a fox, is seen below the magnolia. It belonged to the order Perissodactyla (ungulates with an odd number of toes) which at present is represented only by tapirs, rhinoceroses and horses, but in the Eocene period included many forms. The Hyracotherium had teeth something like those of a pig (bunodont), the limbs were moderately long, and it had four toes on the front and three toes on the hind feet covered by hoofs. Not only was it the ancestor of the horse but it was not far modified from the ancestral form of all the Perissodactyla.

Two kinds of birds are shown in the picture. The flying bird is *Odontopteryx*, a sea-bird about the size of a gannet. Its chief peculiarity was the presence of strongly serrated jaws which were probably covered by horn, and they enabled the bird to seize the fishes on which it lived. The other bird is *Dasornis*, of which little is known. The skull shows that the bird was large, and Sir R. Owen thought that it probably resembled an ostrich.

The other animals are crocodiles which differed little from the living species.

Claygate Beds.—The sandy transition-beds at the top of the London Clay, near London and in Essex, have recently been separated by the Survey as a formation under the name of Claygate Beds (from Claygate, Surrey). They consist of well-defined alternations of sand and clay, sand predominating above and clay below. The formation, where present, is about 50 ft. thick as a rule and is in demand for brick-clay. Fossils are very rare and confined to a few moulds of shells, including *Arctica morrisi*.

Bagshot Beds.—These strata are mainly fine white, buff, and sometimes crimson sands, with occasional seams of pale pipe-clay and local beds of flint-pebble gravel. They form much of the elevated ground in the middle of the London Basin, including the high grounds of Harrow, Hampstead, Chertsey, and Esher ; also, in Essex, Havering-atte-Bower, Brentwood, and Kelvedon Hatch. The full thickness probably does not exceed 120 ft. Fossils are confined to pieces of lignite and plant fragments and a few casts of marine gastropods.

Bracklesham Beds.—These beds are frequently divisible into three parts. The lowest is of clay, usually laminated and lilac tinted but sometimes brown ; a middle division consisting of highly glauconitic sand, often deep green with seams of variegated plastic clay ; and the highest of sand, loam, and clay, with in places, a pebble-band at the base. The total thickness is from about 40 to 65 ft. The strata make bright red bricks known as ' Bagshot ' or Rubber bricks. At St. George's Hill an ironstone band occurs at the junction with the Bagshot Beds and this was formerly worked for iron.

Fossils are found in a few places in the Middle division and indicate deposition in a shallow sea in a warm climate. The more characteristic are :—

Lamellibranchs : *Cardita (Venericor) planicosta; Ostrea plicata.* Gastropod : *Turritella (Ispharina) sulcifera.* Foraminifer : *Nummulites laevigatus.*

Barton Beds.—The Barton Beds are fine-grained, level-bedded, yellow sands, frequently marked off by a pebble-bed from the strata below and with occasional loamy seams near the top. Barton Beds occur in only a few outliers where they have escaped denudation. At St. George's Hill and Chobham Ridges, where best developed, fully 50 ft. are present without indications of an upper limit. The presence of chert in the pebble-bed is of interest, as it indicates that the denudation of the Weald had by then progressed so far as to uncover the Lower Greensand.

Fig. 15 (p. 37) shows the mode of occurrence of the Barton Beds at St. George's Hill. The locality being near the middle of the London Basin, the Eocene strata lie almost horizontally and the Barton Beds are found only on the hilltop.

Fossils are found only occasionally and are marine. Usually they occur as hollow casts in ironstone and a number of them are known also from the Bracklesham Beds, but a few Barton forms have also been recorded.

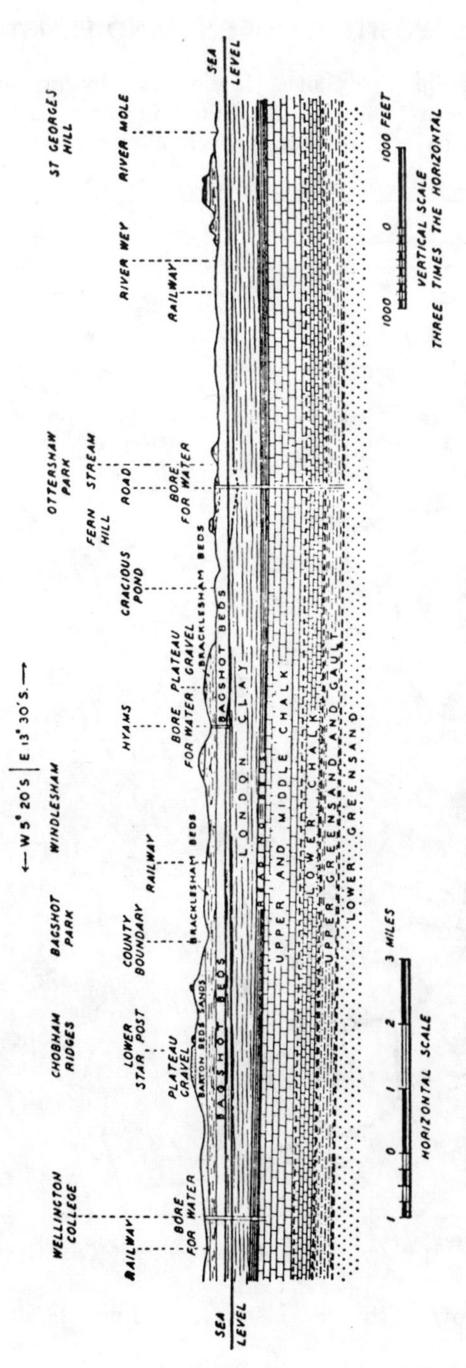

FIG. 15.—*Section through Chobham Ridges and St. George's Hill*

VI. CRAG DEPOSITS: PLIOCENE AND PLEISTOCENE

Crag deposits occur in Essex in a few places, by far the best locality being Walton-on-the-Naze. Relics are found in some parts of the county at the surface, and have also been proved elsewhere in borings through

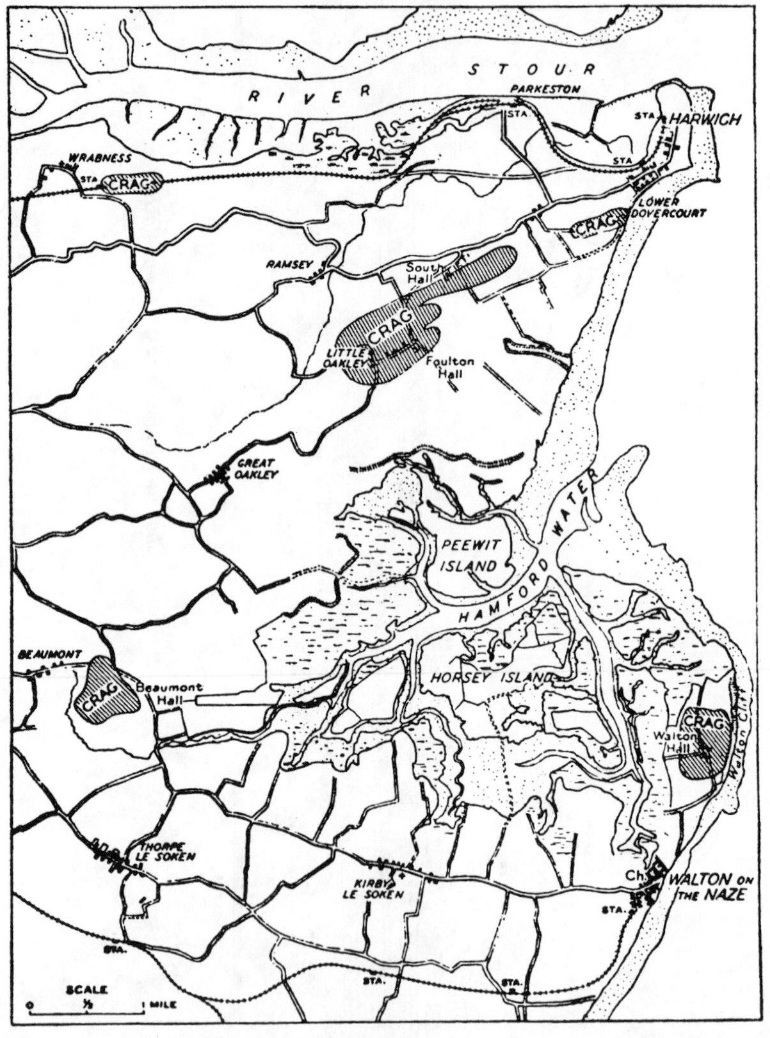

Fig. 16.—*Map of the Waltonian Crag in Essex* (after Harmer)

Drift. The areas covered by these strata are quite small and are shown above in Fig. 16.

The deposits belong to the Waltonian Substage of the Red Crag (now

classified as Pleistocene). They are marine and formed near a shoreline. Shells, often broken and abraded, are abundant, and this fact may indicate the drifting up of material by easterly gales. The climate seems to have been warm temperate. A bed with phosphatic nodules occurs at the base and was formerly worked at Wrabness and Walton.

Common fossils of the Waltonian Red Crag are :—

Lamellibranchs : *Cardium* (*Acanthocardia*) *parkinsoni* ; *Dosinia exoleta* ; *Spisula arcuata* ; *Nucula laevigata*. Gastropods : *Hinia granulata* ; *Neptunea contraria* ; *Nucella incrassata*.

Besides the Crag of Essex there are deposits to the north and south of London which may be of similar age. Between the period of the Eocene and the Great Ice Age there is a long interval of time and the local history of that period is largely lost. Scattered over the North Downs and again in the Chiltern region there are patches of loose deposits, of more than one kind, which are older than the normal Glacial deposits. In the absence of indigenous fossils indirect evidence of age has to be sought, *e.g.* the mineral composition and the elevation above sea-level.

South of the Thames small patches of gravel and sand, resting on Chalk or Reading Beds, occur at Netley Heath, Headley Heath, Sanderstead, Well Hill and some other places. The sites are all shown on the map, Fig. 17 (p. 40). The gravel is mainly composed of much battered flints with some flint-pebbles and pebbles of chert, quartz, etc. The sand is usually coarse, sometimes with scattered pebbles. Microscopically the sands have an assemblage of heavy minerals similar to the material at Lenham, in Kent, which is known to contain fossils of early Pliocene age. At Netley Heath blocks of ferruginous sandstone containing casts of shells have been found and the fossils prove to be of Red Crag (Pleistocene) age, whilst the mineral composition of the blocks differs alike from that of the Lenham Beds and of the Red Crag of Britain. Also these blocks appear to be erratics and the deposit in its present form has been disturbed, presumably by local snow or ice. According to some geologists these deposits rest on a platform cut by wave action during Pliocene time and sloping gently towards London.

North of the Thames the most important of the deposits is a patch found at Little Heath, near Berkhamsted, at an elevation of 550 ft. O.D., where from 5 to 6 ft. of bedded loamy sand rests on 17 ft. of bedded coarse gravel and this on chalk, except for a few inches of chalk residue. As evidence for a Crag age it appears that the sand has a mineral composition similar to that of the North Downs deposits, while, on the other hand, its composition is said to differ from that of some known Reading Beds in the area. Also the plateau on which the deposit rests is said to be part of the plane underlying the Pliocene of Kent, if this plane is produced across the Thames Valley on to the Chiltern plateau, and allowing for a sag along the axis of the London Basin. The constituents of the gravel are almost all flints and flint-pebbles of Eocene character, but a few pebbles of white quartz and lydian stone are found. The gravels have the general aspect of those on the North Downs.

Apart from Little Heath there are only insignificant patches of possible Crag age in the Chiltern region (*see* Fig. 17). There is, however, another deposit, the Pebble Gravel, found on high ground in South Hertfordshire, which has been similarly grouped, although of little later date than the Little Heath deposits.

The Pebble Gravel consists of thin patches of gravel made up mainly of Eocene flint-pebbles and small quartz-pebbles, with a small number of subangular pebbles of flint and of quartz and a few exceptional constituents such as Rhaxella-chert. It was claimed by G. Barrow that Pebble Gravel occurs only at about 400 ft. above Ordnance Datum on the relics of the supposed Pliocene platform, and that when similar gravels are found at lower levels they have been moved and are now not in place : also that they are of fluviatile origin, as distinct from the Little Heath marine deposits, and that the marine deposit (at

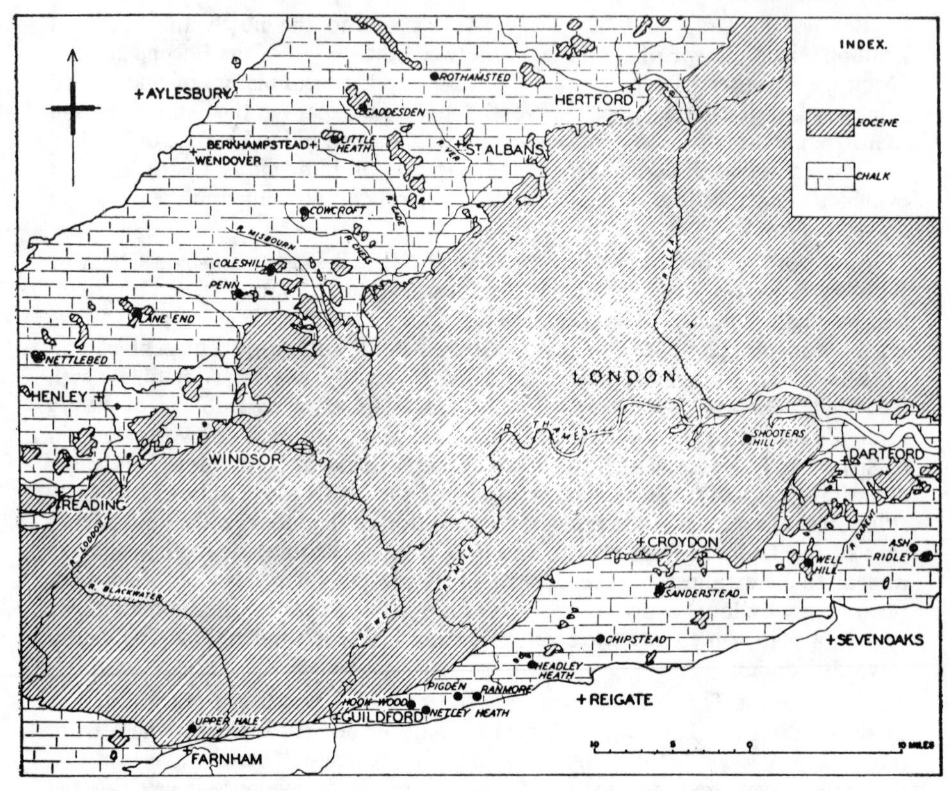

FIG. 17.—*Map showing localities near London where deposits possibly of Crag age occur*

a somewhat higher elevation) is the older. The deposit called Pebbly Clay and Sand (*see* Chapter VII) is regarded as of the same age and origin as the Pebble Gravel, the differences in composition being due to different sources of supply.

On the other hand, it has been argued by the writer that the plane on which Reading Beds lie coincides with that on which the Chiltern deposits stand and that it is better to consider the deposits as possibly Reading Beds than to introduce a new formation, the Pliocene, unless there is strong evidence, such as fossils, for the latter. The deposits at Little Heath differ from normal Reading Beds, but they lie near the margin of the area where these beds were formed, and there is independent evidence (*e.g.* in sarsens and at Lane End, west of High Wycombe) that the Reading Beds became gravelly near their margin. In the Lane End outlier not only do flint gravels containing quartz pebbles and bits of lydian stone occur, but there are large battered flints in undoubted Reading Beds. No constituents that could not have been derived from Reading Beds have been found at Little Heath (*e.g.* Hertfordshire Puddingstone). The value of the evidence of mineral composition is questioned, there being cases known where it has proved to be misleading. Again, the idea that the Pebble Gravel rests on a 400 ft. platform is disputed. The altitude of the patches of gravel lies between 510 ft. and 200 ft. above Ordnance Datum, although it may be said that some have worked their way downwards since they were formed.

It is agreed that the Pebbly Clay and Sand is similar in age and origin to the Pebble Gravel, but the former grades into Clay-with-flints (*see* Chapter VII), from which it is separable with difficulty, and if the Pebble Gravel and the Pebbly Clay and Sand are of Crag age presumably so is some at least of the Clay-with-flints, yet there are good reasons for regarding it as of glacial origin.

Finally, masses of rocks containing Red Crag fossils have been found by Survey Officers embedded in Clay-with-flints at Rothamsted, Hertfordshire, and we have seen that Red Crag fossils have also been found in loose blocks at Netley Heath on the North Downs. These masses are clearly boulders and both deposits are disturbed, but it is not known whence the boulders were brought.

It has been said that the fossiliferous blocks found at Netley Heath and Rothamsted, though not in place, nevertheless proved that marine Crag deposits must have been deposited in the vicinity.

Prof. S. W. Wooldridge has found a gravelly deposit capping London Clay at Lane End. This deposit must be newer than the London Clay below, and as it is said to be very like the material at Little Heath the inference is that Lane End capping and Little Heath material are of the same age.

The following are a few of the Red Crag Fossils from Netley Heath :—

Lamellibranchs : *Corbulomya complanata ; Cardium* (*Cerastoderma*) *edule* var. *edulinum*. Gastropods : *Hinia propinqua ; Nucella incrassata.*

Red Crag fossils from Rothamsted include :—

Lamellibranchs : *Mytilus edulis ; Barnea cylindrica.* Gastropod : *Hinea granulata.*

VII. PLEISTOCENE AND RECENT

The base of the Red Crag has recently been adopted as the dividing line between Pliocene and Pleistocene. All deposits later than Crag, whether belonging to the Pleistocene System or still later (Recent), are called ' Drifts '. They are found in more or less extensive patches scattered over the area and unconformable to the ' Solid Rocks '. They offer difficult problems as regards their relative ages owing to their sporadic character preventing a direct arrangement in order of superposition. But there are other difficulties : for example, whilst the main mass of the Clay-with-flints is amongst the oldest of the Drifts it is still being added to, to a small extent, by the continued solution of chalk. Also there are two Chalky Boulder Clays in a few places, such as Hertford, and they may represent two advances of the ice ; but the lower one occurs in thin and irregular lenses in sand and gravel, not far below the upper clay, and it may be that the two belong to one episode in the Ice Age. Again, the age relations of the river terraces to the boulder-clays are as yet not very clear. Below is a list of drifts arranged, as far as possible, in order of increasing age :—

Alluvium and Peat
River Gravel. Flood Plain Terrace with Arctic Bed
Taplow Brickearth
River Gravel. Taplow Terrace
Boyn Hill Brickearth
River Gravel. Boyn Hill Terrace
Dry Valley Gravel ; Gravel opposite Chalk Gaps ; Coombe Deposits
Boulder Clay with Glacial Sand and Gravel and Laminated Clay
' Plateau Gravel '
Clay-with-flints and associated Pebbly Clay and Sand
Pebble Gravel

Many local names are in use, *e.g.* Warley Gravel ; and some isolated occurrences are difficult to place.

Pebble Gravel.—This deposit is, broadly, the same as the Westleton Beds described by Prestwich. The Pebble Gravel is composed chiefly of flint-pebbles derived from Eocene deposits with a variable proportion of small, white, well-rounded quartz-pebbles, probably derived directly or indirectly from the Lower Greensand. Other ingredients often present are partially rounded flints, occasional fragments of lydian stone, chert, and siliceous sandstone. For a discussion of its age see *ante*, p. 39.

Pebble Gravel is found in patches on the Tertiary plateau north of London, from Oxhey Wood to Hertford Heath. With the descent of the plateau towards the Thames the gravel ceases, the southerly limit being near Totteridge, Botany Bay, and Claysmore.

East of the Lea, in Essex, various names have been given to the gravelly patches, and it is not certain that the high-level gravels are all of the same age. However, the Pebble Gravel is known to occur in Epping Forest, Havering-atte-Bower, etc., and probably the Warley Gravel belongs here also. Other high-level gravels of Essex, such as those of Danbury and Tiptree Heath, contain additional constituents, such as abundant quartzites and black Palaeozoic cherts. Opinions differ as to the significance of these constituents ; they may have been introduced into the area by melting ice and incorporated in previously existing gravels, or the deposits may be ordinary glacial gravels and therefore newer than the Pebble Gravel.

Clay-with-flints and associated Pebbly Clay and Sand.—These deposits are confined to the Chalk areas where they cap the high ground. The Clay-with-flints proper is composed, in part, of the insoluble residue left by solution of Chalk-with-flints, but this material alone consists almost entirely of angular flints with little interstitial clay, whereas the deposit is a brown loamy clay containing abundant angular flints stained brown throughout, and some flint-pebbles. The additional clay and the flint-pebbles are derived from the waste of Eocene outliers which capped the chalk and decayed there. The actual Clay-with-flints is a mixture of these Chalk and Eocene derivatives rearranged by local snow or ice towards the (local) commencement of the ice-age, although the mass is being added to slightly wherever percolation of water causes the underlying chalk to be dissolved.

In the Chiltern Hills Clay-with-flints passes laterally in places into what, for lack of a better name, has been called Pebbly Clay and Sand. This deposit is composed of the same constituents as Clay-with-flints but in different proportions, the materials being mainly Eocene refuse, *i.e.* flint-pebbles, reddish clay and pale-coloured sand. The much larger proportion of flint-pebbles to angular flints and the patches of sand distinguish Pebbly Clay and Sand from Clay-with-flints. There is a tendency for it to appear on the south side of Clay-with-flints in the Chiltern country owing to the slope of the platform on which it rests, in that direction. The Eocene outliers, of the waste of which it is composed, would be overriden by chalk debris from the crest of the Chiltern escarpment, so by admixture making Clay-with-flints, but the bulk of the Eocene refuse would be pushed lower down the slope. It is impossible to find a clear line of demarcation between these two associated deposits which have a common mode of origin. Both deposits are free from far-travelled constituents ; an important distinction between them and some other drifts.

From time to time particularly good sections are exposed at Walter's Ash, near High Wycombe (*see* Plate III). Here blocks of hard white sandstone (sarsens) sometimes of enormous size, are found embedded in red clay, with masses of loamy clay and flints surrounding them. There is no doubt that the sarsens and the red clay are derived from destroyed masses of Reading Beds. Exceptionally, laminated sandy brickearth is found in the deposits at Walter's Ash, while brickearth fit for use for brickmaking occurs in a number of places where the Reading Beds clay comprises the bulk of the deposit. In a few places, *e.g.* at Gaddesden Row, about three and a half miles north-north-west of Hemel Hempstead, flint implements have been found in the brickearth, proving that the material, although apparently Reading Beds, is merely the debris of that formation.

On the North Downs Clay-with-flints and associated Pebbly Clay and Sand occur just as in the Chiltern area, although the two are not readily separable. South of Croydon chert and sandstone fragments from the Lower Greensand have been found, indicating a southern origin. The method of formation may have been from a local debris accumulated under periglacial conditions, but as in this region the dip-slope is northwards the materials tend to be moved in that direction.

Undoubted Glacial Deposits.—These comprise Boulder Clay, Sand and Gravel, and Laminated Clay associated with the Sand and Gravel. Boulder-clay, the ground moraine of an ice-sheet, consists mainly of unsorted materials formed in part by erosive action, in part from the rock debris accumulated by weathering on the surface of the land. The coarser material washed from the boulder-clay or from morainic or englacial accumulations was deposited by glacial streams as sand and gravel, either on land or in lakes. Fine debris settled quietly in temporary lakes to form laminated clays and silts.

The principal ice-carried Drifts may be divided according to composition into three main kinds. In Essex there is clay with a chalky matrix (Chalky Boulder Clay). In Hertfordshire and Buckinghamshire, north of the Chiltern Hills, the clayey matrix, while still chalky, is composed mainly of Jurassic materials (Chalky-Jurassic Boulder Clay). In Oxfordshire the oldest drift, which is generally a loamy gravel and only occasionally boulder-clay, is characterized by abundant Bunter material (Bunter Drift), although this constituent also occurs in the other two boulder-clays to some extent. Gravel with Bunter pebbles extends through the Goring Gap into South Buckinghamshire.

The differences in composition are due to the kinds of rocks over which the ice passed. Thus, in Essex the ice passed over large areas of the Chalk, whereas the more westerly section of the ice-sheet, which came over the Jurassic areas of the Wash and Cambridgeshire, had its composition modified accordingly.

The ice coming over Cambridgeshire impinged upon the Chiltern Hills but could not override them west of about Hitchin. East of that place the hills are lower and the ice was able to penetrate through certain gaps, notably one along the line of the new railway from Stevenage to Hertford. Still farther east the hills were overridden by ice and broad spreads of drift cover much of the country. The ice that penetrated through the Stevenage gap and that from farther east was enabled to spread out behind the Chilterns westward to St. Albans and southward to Finchley, rising like a flood to an elevation of about 420 ft. above Ordnance Datum.

The Chalky Boulder Clay probably once covered most of Essex but has since been broken up by river denudation into irregularly shaped areas. Although at present it does not extend into the low ground north of the Thames estuary, this may be due to subsequent denudation. It consists mainly of a bluish-grey sandy clay containing stones and boulders which, together with the clayey matrix, were brought by the ice from East Anglia and the North Sea. Stones from Lincolnshire and Yorkshire and pebbles from the Bunter are not uncommon, but the great majority of the stones are flints from the chalk and fragments of Jurassic rocks. When the material is fresh, chalk shows prominently in the clay, but by weathering, this constituent, and small limestone boulders, are dissolved out and a brown loamy clay results. Where the boulder-clay rests directly on London Clay the bottom part is largely composed of that rock, but normally chalk is an important constituent. Occasionally gravel lenticles occur in the clay. Thicknesses up to about 140 ft. of boulder-clay are recorded.

The Chalky-Jurassic Boulder Clay was formed by the same ice-sheet as the Chalky Boulder Clay and there is a gradation from one into the other, as the chalk becomes less and the Jurassic constituents more marked. The boulder-clay in Hertfordshire contains mainly Jurassic material which came from Lincolnshire, Northamptonshire, and Huntingdonshire, and not only spread out in front of the Chilterns but passed through the Stevenage gap to unite near Ware with the more chalky clay. Occasionally, as at Ware, boulders are found which must have been brought across the North Sea from Scandinavia.

The third kind of glacial drift is largely composed of Triassic material and notably Bunter pebbles from the Midlands. Boulder-clay occurs in the Vale of Moreton and just enters Oxfordshire *via* the Evenlode Valley. It is a plastic clay, sometimes loamy and generally red-brown in colour but occasionally grey. Stones are scattered throughout, mostly small pebbles, but boulders are not uncommon. The clay does not exceed 8 ft. in thickness. The bulk of this drift, however, is in the form of isolated patches of loamy sand and gravel which extend along the Evenlode and then continue along the Thames Valley, capping the high ground on both sides of the river at intervals, as far as Bourne End. Here it leaves the river to continue across country : a fact that lends support to the view of the writer that in Pre-Glacial times the Thames flowed through Rickmansworth and Hertford and that the drift followed the old valley for some distance.

Sand and gravel are found in connection with the boulder-clay and usually appear from underneath it where the ground falls from the plateau level, as in the sides of valleys. The deposits are composed of very roughly bedded sands, from mere silt to coarse grits, with wedges of gravel as well as scattered stones in the sands. These stones vary from the size of a pea to occasional boulders up to a foot long. The indications of formation by tumultuous floods, *i.e.* the current-bedding and mixed sizes of the constituents, are marked.

Fossils which were contemporaneous (as distinct from fossils derived from the rocks swept up by the ice) are exceedingly rare in boulder-clay. In the gravels contemporary fossils are much less rare and include bones.

Plateau Gravel.—On the older geological maps there are many areas coloured as Plateau Gravels, meaning simply high-level gravels. With increased knowledge a good many of these patches have been placed in one or other of the drifts listed on p. 42, but a number still remain unclassified and retain the old name for lack of a better one. The more important areas of Plateau Gravel left on the maps are situated on the south side of the Thames and in Oxfordshire.

South of the Thames the largest of many scattered patches of Plateau Gravel is that covering much of Bagshot Heath and Chobham Ridge. These gravels form two types according to their composition : (1) contains many small pebbles of vein-quartz associated with abundant flints derived from Chalk and Eocene rocks, but no Lower Greensand chert ; (2) is similar, but with fewer vein-quartz pebbles and with Lower Greensand chert fragments. The former kind occurs west of a line extending roughly from Reading through Strathfield-saye and up the Lodden Valley ; the latter is found east of this line. The absence of Bunter pebbles, so common in the Glacial Sand and Gravel (p. 44), suggests that the Plateau Gravel was formed before ice brought Bunter debris into the Thames Valley. It is possible that the Plateau Gravel includes materials of more than one mode of origin : the western material frequently contains clay and may have affinities with the 'Pebbly Clay and Sand' ; also it is often unstratified. The gravels east of the River Lodden and Reading contain cherts derived from the south and are probably the debris from periodically frozen high ground around Hindhead.

The Oxfordshire Plateau Gravel consists of red-brown clay, loam occasionally with some sand, and pebbles of all sizes. It is rarely bedded and then but roughly. In addition to battered flints there are sandstone, quartzite probably from the Bunter, white quartz and lydian stone. Dr. S. .K Sandford thinks that the deposit was formed under the sea during an early Pleistocene submergence, but there is still uncertainty about its mode of origin.

Dry Valley Gravel and 'Gravels opposite Chalk Gaps'.—The Chiltern Hills are cut through by a number of valleys the heads of which are now dry, and in consequence they are known as 'Wind-gaps'. Narrow strips of gravel occupy the floors and are continuous down-stream with ordinary river gravel. Up-stream, however, the dry-valley gravels sometimes actually pass through the gaps in the hills and spread out as terraces on the steep face of the escarpment, *e.g.* at Tring and at Dagnall. In the case of the Wendover Gap bones of mammoth have been found in the deposit.

The position of these gravels, within and in front of the wind-gaps, is abnormal, and their mode of origin is best understood by considering the block diagram of the Chiltern Hills, Fig. 18 (p. 47). This diagram displays, in the first place, the prominent escarpment of the Chalk, the subdivisions of which may be seen on the edges of the block. On the surface of the block only the drifts are shown. Covering the plateau, in the background, we see Clay-with-flints, and in the wind-gaps of Wendover and Tring is seen the Dry Valley Gravel with its remarkable lateral extension, in the case of the Tring Gap, on to the front of the escarpment. The gravel rises in altitude up-valley towards the observer until it reaches the highest point, when, instead of dying out, it passes through the gap and expands in right and left lobes which rest on shelves in front of the escarpment and rise steadily in altitude to about 610 ft. above sea-level, although the highest point within the gap itself is only about 430 ft. above Ordnance Datum. An explanation of their curious position is that in Pleistocene times an ice-sheet advancing from the north impinged on the Chiltern Hills escarpment but was unable to override it in the Wendover-Tring section. With the waning of the ice, floods of water were let loose and formed a lake between the hills and the retreating ice. The waters of this lake rose until their level reached cols in the escarpment where Wendover and Tring now stand. Here they overflowed into valleys on the dip-slope of the Chiltern plateau, cutting gorges very rapidly in the soft chalk. At that time the deep-seated chalk would be frozen and impervious, whilst the top material (in summer at least) would have thawed and be in soft condition, offering little resistance to cutting, once the lake began to overflow. Very soon the lake fell below the level of the Wendover Gap, 500 ft. O.D., but continued to drain through the Tring gap, which was cut down to about 430 ft. above Ordnance Datum.

Whilst the overflow from the lake was cutting the gaps some of the Clay-with-flints was washed down the Chiltern escarpment tumultuously by the melting of snow or ice which covered the plateau, and was carried through the

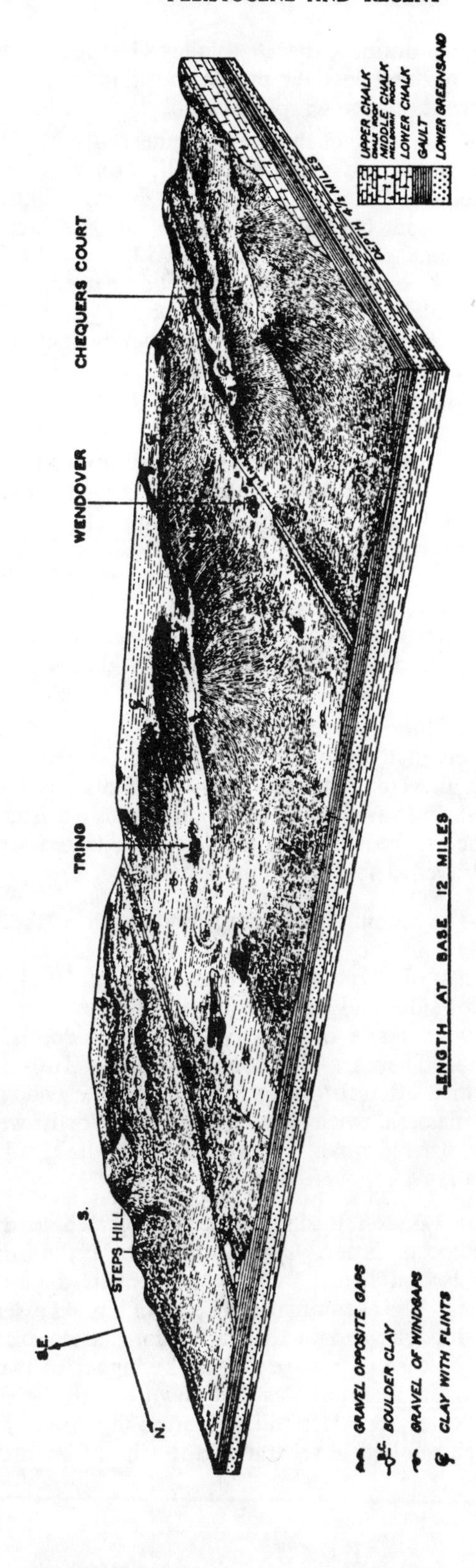

FIG. 18.—*Panoramic view of part of the Chiltern Hills*

Note.—Owing to perspective the rocks appear to rise, instead of to dip, towards London

gaps, so that when the lake drained, the Dry Valley Gravels, formed from the Clay-with-flints debris, were left in their present positions ; that is, not only within the gaps but in front of the escarpment also.

The block-diagram shows three of the deep channels cut out of the chalk by the melt-waters from the plateau. One, at Steps Hill, is on the extreme left and the other two are in Chequers Court Park. The best examples, however, occur between Steps Hill and Luton, beyond the limits of the diagram. The Steps Hill channel (Plate V) commences in the union of two U-shaped gullies. At the junction the main channel begins abruptly and follows a curving course for about three-quarters of a mile, before it ends rather suddenly on the plain in front of the hills. The channel has a flat bottom of nearly constant width and the slope of the sides is very steep, about 45°, with a valley depth of about 110 ft. at the head. The lower end of the channel would mark the level of the lake at the time of formation.

In the foreground of the block diagram the 'Gravels opposite Chalk Gaps', formed on the lake floor, are to be seen. These gravels are composed of flints mostly small and decayed, some flint-pebbles and rounded pieces of chalk, all derived from the Chilterns. They spread as thin deposits over a considerable area but usually form a mere skin of gravel, except opposite the Wendover and Tring gaps, as shown, where they are as much as 5 ft. thick. Their thin wide-spread character is an indication of deposition in the waters of a lake. On the front edge of the block is seen a small cap of ordinary glacial drift containing far-travelled stones.

It is evident that the Chiltern escarpment must have existed in its present position before the gravels that rest on its slope were deposited ; also that the plateau has been partly dissected since the Clay-with-flints cover was formed. Had the present dry valleys at Wendover and Tring been in existence when the ice advanced against the escarpment it would have penetrated into them and doubtless have left far-travelled stones therein as evidence.

Coombe Deposits.—The Coombe deposits found south of the Thames are probably similar in origin to the Dry Valley Gravel of the Chiltern region. Coombe deposits consist of structureless masses of material which have descended from the valley sides and lie on the floors of valleys (or ' coombes '). Consequently they may be made of any available rock debris, *e.g.* chalk-rubble, or Eocene strata. They are also connected with ' Trail ' or ' Head ', the tumbled material which often forms a surface layer over wide areas due to movement of semi-fluid masses down a slope. Some of these drifts were probably accumulated on deeply frozen ground. Not uncommonly the Head merges into the Flood Plain Terrace gravel.

River Deposits.—The London Basin has been subjected to a number of changes of level since Pliocene times. One result has been the formation of a complex series of gravels and loams forming terraces in the valleys of the Thames and its tributaries. The accumulations being of limited extent and often similar in aspect, it is difficult to date the individual masses except by their relative elevations. In the case of river deposits the higher of two terraces is usually the older one, for its material was laid down before the river had cut down to the level of the lower one. It is still difficult to fit these terraces and the Glacial deposits into a chronological scheme and it will not be attempted here.

The river terraces of the Thames are three in number; in order of decreasing age they are :—

Boyn Hill Terrace
Taplow Terrace
Flood Plain Terrace

The Boyn Hill Terrace was formerly called the 100 ft. Terrace and the Taplow Terrace the 50 ft. Terrace—unfortunate names, for the terraces alter in elevation above sea-level when followed along the valleys, although the change is small over long distances. The new names are taken from Boyn Hill and Taplow, both near Maidenhead, where the upper and middle terraces are well developed. Each terrace consists of a sheet of gravel and sand with a deposit of brickearth (really an alluvium) over it, and each terrace represents a period of aggradation by alluvial deposition following one of uplift and erosion.

In sections the appearance of all three terrace-gravels is the same and they also resemble fluvio-glacial gravel. To a limited extent fossil evidence helps to date the terraces; thus the musk-ox (*Ovibos moschatus* Zimm.) occurs notably in the Taplow Terrace. The Boyn Hill Terrace fossils, taken together, indicate a fairly warm climate, the Taplow fossils one that is cooler, and the Flood Plain fossils include indicators of an Arctic climate. The faunas show no sharp divisions, however, and mollusca in the finer deposits usually betoken mild climatic phases. Some assistance is also obtained from flint implements, but these do not necessarily fix the age of the terrace that contains them.

The gravels are composed mostly of flints derived from the Chalk, and flint-pebbles derived from the Eocene, both kinds mainly, however, at second-hand ; and there is a small proportion of pebbles of sandstone, quartzite, etc., obtained from the destruction of older gravels. The matrix is sand of varying degrees of coarseness. The thickness may attain to 30 or 40 ft. or more, but is usually less. Where the brickearth which covers the gravel has escaped denudation it may be up to 20 or more feet thick and is a reddish-brown loamy clay.

The Boyn Hill, or highest terrace, covers the least area because much of the original material has been since denuded and incorporated in later and lower terraces. When excavated it is found that the gravel rests on a terrace at the top of a buried bluff or steep slope of ' solid ' rock, but this may not be visible at the surface owing to downwash making a steady slope from Boyn Hill to Taplow terraces. In many cases, however, the two terraces are separated by a strip of exposed ' solid '. Fragments of the top terrace occur between Burnham and Iver, also south of Hillingdon, in Islington, Wanstead, Chadwell, etc. South of the Thames they occur at Wandsworth and Clapham Common (Fig. 19, p. 50), Croydon, Dartford Heath and Swanscombe.

The best exposures of the Boyn Hill Terrace are at Swanscombe, where they are excavated to obtain the underlying chalk. This locality has long been famous for its stone-implements and an investigation was made by Messrs. H. Dewey and R. A. Smith to discover if the different layers of the terrace material were associated with different styles of implements.

In Fig. 20 (p. 51) a section of Barnfield (or Milton Street) pit is shown, with a scale marking the thicknesses in feet. In the Lower Gravel primitive implements of Early Clactonian type are found together with a species of elephant (*Palaeoloxodon antiquus*). In the Middle Gravel hand axes of Acheulian types occur. Parts of a human skull were found in this division in 1935-6.

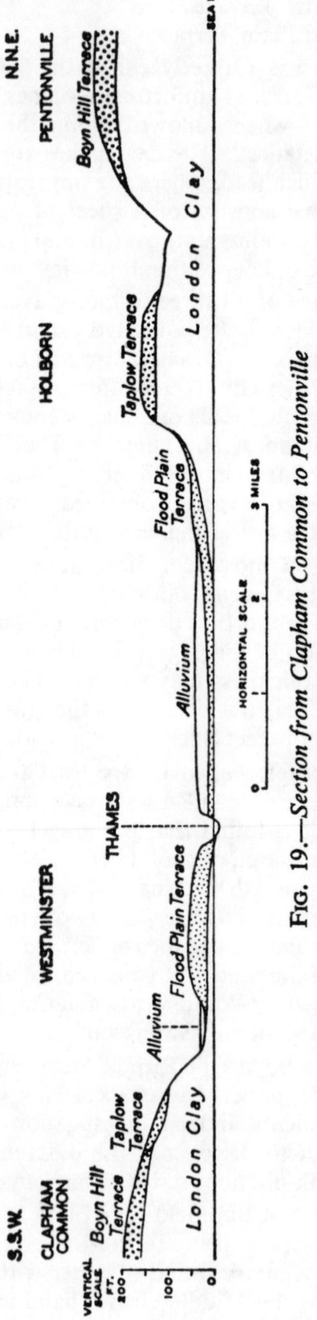

FIG. 19.—*Section from Clapham Common to Pentonville*

To show the relations of the Boyn Hill, Taplow, and Flood Plain River Terraces

The Taplow and Flood Plain Terrace gravels are to be distinguished from the Boyn Hill Terrace and one another chiefly by their respective elevations above the valley. It should be remembered, however, that it is the level of the bottom of the deposit, not of the surface, that is to be considered. The brickearth corresponding to the Flood Plain Gravel is the modern alluvium. Both terraces

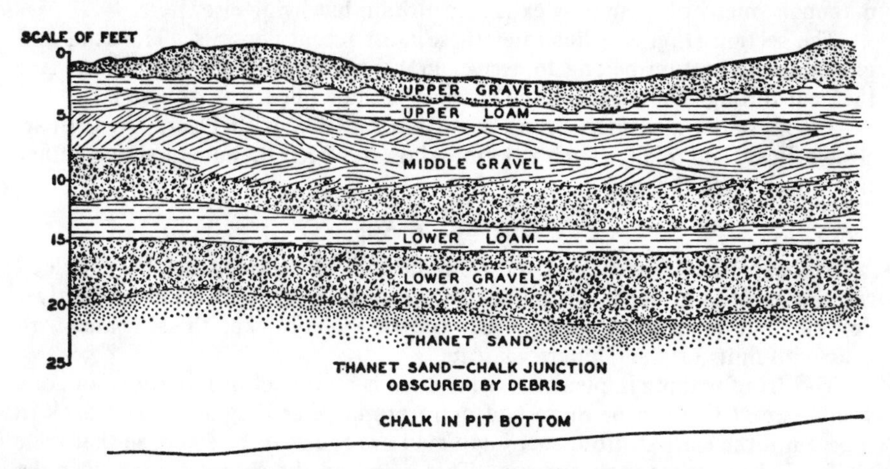

FIG. 20.—*Diagrammatic section of Gravels at Barnfield Pit, Swanscombe*

are much more extensive than the Boyn Hill and their distribution may be seen on maps. In addition to Fig. 19, p. 50, Fig. 21, p. 51, is given to show the relations of these terraces. The latter section is taken along Exhibition Road past the Geological Museum.

In London the Flood Plain gravels descend below the present level of the Thames, and eastwards they continue far below sea-level. It seems possible that this terrace comprises two periods, the first following the deposition of the Taplow brickearth, during which the higher part of the Flood Plain Gravel was deposited, followed by another period of elevation during which the river cut a deep gorge-like channel from Brentford downwards to the sea. The channel then became filled up with gravel practically to the level of that of the first period, so that the two gravels can rarely be distinguished.

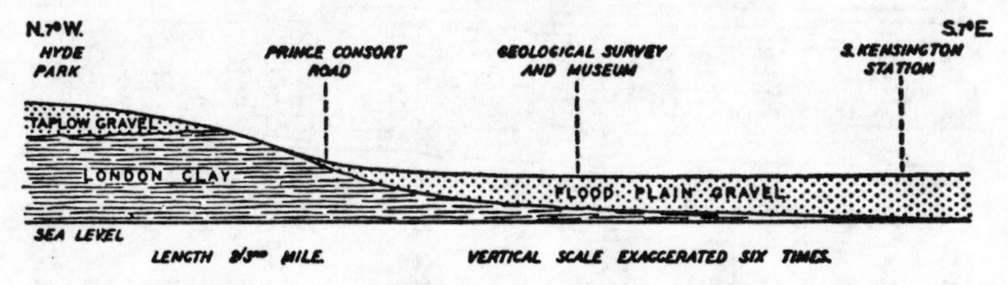

FIG. 21.—*Section along Exhibition Road, South Kensington*

Beds containing Arctic plants have been found in the Flood Plain terraces at several localities in the Lea Valley, accompanied by other fossils showing a cold climate, including the mammoth *Mammuthus primigenius.*

Alluvium and Peat.—The silty and clayey material spread by modern rivers in flood-time is called alluvium. Streaks of sand and gravel are sometimes present and indicate exceptional floods. In marshy localities peat is formed by the accumulation of vegetation, particularly moss and rushes. Alluvium dates from the Neolithic stone-age to the present day and some of the peaty deposits are of Roman date. These late deposits contain interesting fossils, especially mammals, many of them now extinct in Britain but living elsewhere.

The section (Fig. 22) illustrates these most recent deposits. The sand and gravel at the bottom belong to a river gravel on which peat formed. A river then cut through the peat and the channel became filled with alluvium.

Amongst the mammals found fossil are the Elk, Irish Deer, Urus, Boar, Brown Bear, and Wolf. Their extermination has been by human action rather than by climatic changes.

The Stone Age

The superficial deposits of the London and Thames District have yielded remains of Man in numerous places. For the most part they occur in the river deposits, but important finds have also been made in brickearth associated with Clay-with-flints on the Chiltern plateau.

The art of making implements from stone is a product of evolution, and one would expect them to be more and more primitive as they are traced back in time, until the earliest products of ape-man are found to be so crude that their artificial character is very obscure. This is indeed the case if we consider the older artifacts (specimens of human work), but stone-implements attained their highest quality fairly early and as Man turned his attention to new materials, such as bone or horn, the workmanship of such stone-implements as were still made became inferior to that of earlier times, when stone alone was worked. The most primitive forms found in the area described are the *Eoliths* picked up on the North Downs. In these the flint has a crust of an ochreous tint and they are said to be patinated. The patina is due to a slow weathering process which turns the outer part of a flint white and the resulting absorbent crust (the patina) may become stained by ferruginous matter from the matrix in

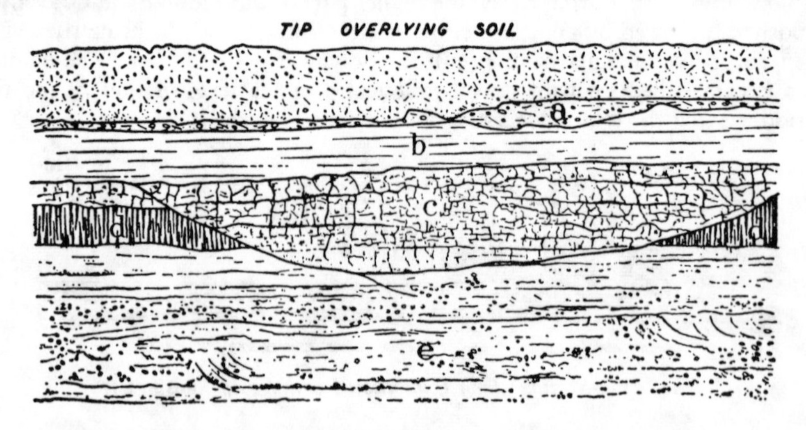

FIG. 22.—*Section at Albert Dock Extension*
a=Soil ; *b*=Alluvium, clayey ; *c*=Alluvium, silty ; *d*=Peat ; *e*=Sand and Gravel

which it has been buried ; consequently, patination on an implement is often regarded as an indication of antiquity. Some of the eoliths would be generally accepted as implements, but they grade into others the human origin of which is dubious.

Next in age are the *Palaeoliths*, the artificial origin of which there can be no doubt. They show several types of culture, named from the original localities in Europe where they have been discovered. Transitional from the eoliths we have the more definite implements of the Early Clactonian, (from Clacton, Essex) which are followed by the *Chelles* type (from Chelles on the Marne, ten miles above Paris). These grade into the *St. Acheul* type (from St. Acheul, near Amiens) and the difference between them is not easy to define. St. Acheul implements occur abundantly at Swanscombe, mainly in the Middle Gravel of that place (*see* Fig. 20 p. 51, and Fig. 23, p. 54), and some artifacts from there are doubtfully referred to the Chelles type.

The next stage of culture is that of *Le Moustier* and shows a distinct improvement, for instead of trimming a flint-nodule and using the core as an implement, it became usual to prepare one side of a flint and then by a single blow to separate the worked part from the core. This gave a much thinner and lighter implement than the older method. These ' flake ' implements are also known as the *Levallois* type, and the trimmed nodule from which they are struck is called a ' tortoise-core ', owing to the shape. The implements are found in the Taplow terrace deposits and were probably produced by Neanderthal man.

The next culture in age is that of *Aurignac* and *Solutré*, introducing smaller types of flint-implements, but although artifacts of this type are recorded in the Flood Plain terrace from the site of the Admiralty, Whitehall, they are not known to occur elsewhere in our district.

In the Flood Plain terrace there are many worn implements derived from the older gravels, but at Uxbridge and a few other places indigenous implements of *La Madelaine* (from a place in the Dordogne) man have been found. In this culture the first indications of Art shown by Aurignac man are further developed. Flint was being largely replaced by bone, antlers, and tusks and these are ornamented with engraved images of animals and other objects, while the flint-implements themselves are of inferior workmanship.

Implements have been found in brickearth on the Chiltern plateau at Caddington and Gaddesdon Row, not far from Luton. They belong to the close of the St. Acheul and commencement of Le Moustier periods. The top few feet of the deposit show signs of disturbance and in them water-worn early Chelles implements have been found.

Neolithic (the newer stone age) flakes are found frequently in the soils of the district, as well as in peaty layers in the alluvium, and similar ones were produced as late as the Roman period.

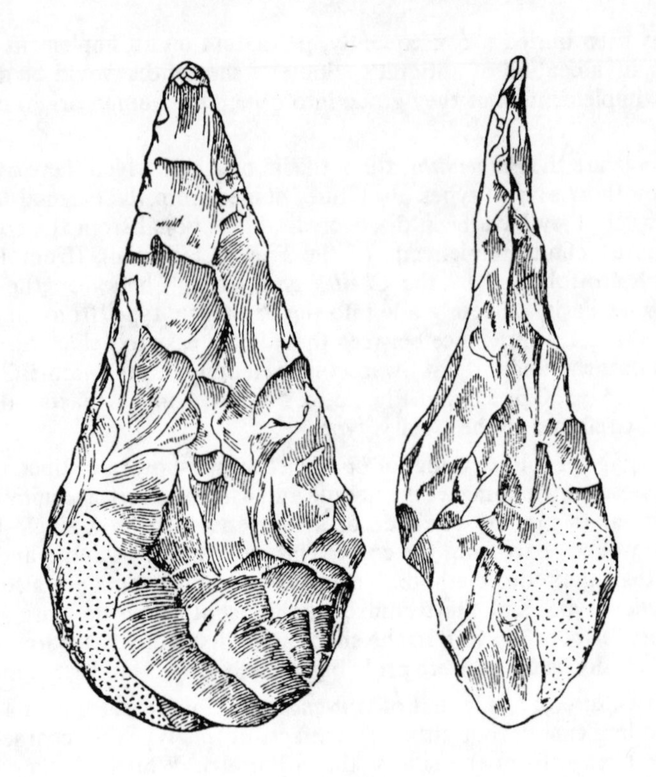

FIG. 23.—*Flint implements* (W. G. Smith)
The upper implement, of St. Acheul type, is from Lower Clapton
The lower implement, a chopper of " tea-cosy " pattern is from **Stoke Newington**

VIII. ECONOMIC PRODUCTS

ALTHOUGH the district is not rich in economic minerals it is well supplied with the raw materials of the building industry and there is a considerable output of bricks, cement, sand and gravel, and road metal. Owing to the enormous population of the London area these materials are in great demand and most of them can be supplied locally. A few of the chief economic mineral products will be discussed briefly.

Bricks and Tiles.—Until about 1835 the bricks used in London were stock-bricks made from dustbin refuse and road sweepings mixed with clay and largely burnt by their own combustible contents. Later, stock-bricks came to be made of London Clay and chalk mixed with coal-dust.

The choice of materials used for bricks has altered greatly since the in-coming of modern machines : whereas, formerly, soft weathered clays alone were used, these are now in little demand and the majority of bricks are made from hard clay or shale. The clay originally used in this area was a sandy or silty weathered clay called *brickearth*, found in Quaternary deposits ; some was formed in lakes or silting-up rivers. Much of the brickearth of the London area has been used up, but the industry is still carried on in a few places. The staple London brick at present is the Fletton type, made from Oxford Clay, near Peterborough and elsewhere. This is made of unweathered clay or shale.

In the district described bricks are made of Reading Beds around Bracknell, and near Hemel Hempstead, etc. At Epsom and Ewell the greenish loams at the base of the Reading Beds contain a fireclay from which firebricks were formerly made. Loams from the Blackheath Beds are used at Bickley, Kent. London Clay is extensively used, particularly the loamy top called the Claygate Beds. Of Quaternary clays the brickearth included in the Clay-with-flints has been worked in the Chiltern country and Glacial clays at Hill End, near St. Albans, and at Ware.

Drain-pipes and tiles are made of clays similar to those used for bricks. ' Sand-lime ' bricks are made from Thanet Sand and chalk.

Portland Cement.—Cement was originally made from argillaceous limestone, and Parker, the first manufacturer, about 1791, used chiefly London Clay septaria. At present Portland Cement is by far the commonest variety.

The ingredients of Portland Cement are clay and limestone ; in the Thames Valley the limestone used is chalk. There are two processes, the wet and the dry, and the former is used in the Northfleet area. The clay is either mud shipped from the River Medway or the clay strata above the chalk. The two constituents are mixed and ground with water in correct proportions, until the resultant slurry is so fine that 96 to 97 per cent. of the solid matter will pass through a sieve having 32,400 holes per sq. in.

The slurry is pumped into rotating kilns where it is first dried, then, as the material moves on, the limestone is decomposed, and finally chemical combination takes place and clinker is formed at about 2,800° F. The clinker is in small balls which, after cooling, are ground to impalpable powder. During grinding the setting time of the cement is fixed by the addition of steam or gypsum. Under the revised British Standards Specification the proportion as calculated in chemical equivalents, of lime (CaO) to the silica (SiO_2) and the alumina (Al_2O_3) together, must not be greater than 2·85.

Gravel and Sand.—Gravel for concrete is a very important material and the district possesses large quantities of suitable flint-gravel. The main sources of supply are the alluvial and glacial gravels and in these the sandy matrix also largely composed of flint, is frequently sharp and suitable for use as a building sand.

Moulding Sand is obtained chiefly from the Thanet Sand, extensively worked around Woolwich for home and export trades. At Charlton the Thanet Beds are 60 ft. thick and the lowest 10 ft. or so (' strong loam ' or ' blackfoot ') were used for brass casting, whilst the 14 ft. of sand above this (' mild loam ') were used for iron moulding. Sands for moulding are obtained also from Bagshot Beds at Billericay, Essex ; from Bagshot Sands, south of Coppid Beech Lane, Bracknell ; from the Shotover Grit Sands of Kimmeridge Clay age; and from Lower Greensand at Stone, near Aylesbury.

Glass Sands are rare. That from the Lower Greensand at Stone is of two qualities, one of them superior to Belgian sand. It occurs in 4-ft. to 6-ft. seams. In the Thanet Beds at Charlton the upper part above the moulding sand, about 36 ft. of white sand, was formerly used for making amber-coloured glass.

At Chobham the Bagshot Sand locally contains a 3-ft. seam of exceedingly fine sand, used for polishing.

Stonesfield Slates.—Stonesfield has yielded ' slates ' since Roman times. The Stonesfield Slate formation is from 2 to 6 ft. thick, and one, two, or three layers, in different places, yield suitable stone. The ' slate ' is really a thin-bedded sandy limestone and has been displaced for roofing almost entirely by tiles and true cleaved slates.

Building Stone and Road Metal.—The various limestones of the Jurassic System have been used extensively in the past as building stones. Some of them have not stood the test of time satisfactorily, as is shown by some of the Oxford University buildings. Probably the Headington (Corallian) and Swindon (Portland Beds) stones are the best known building stones from the district. Many of the harder rocks have been used for local buildings, and they also supply aggregate for concrete, and road-metal. The hard beds in the Chalk have been used and also the flints so common in the Upper Chalk.

Sarsens, derived from Tertiary beds, have been used from time immemorial for buildings and road-metal. Large sarsens from the Reading Beds are found embedded in Clay-with-flints at Naphill, near High Wycombe, Bucks. These are of white saccharoidal sandstone with siliceous cement and form first-class building stone and setts, but the supply is small. The chippings are used for road-metal.

In the Chalk area flints derived from Clay-with-flints have been and still are used. These flints are tough owing to long weathering and do little harm to

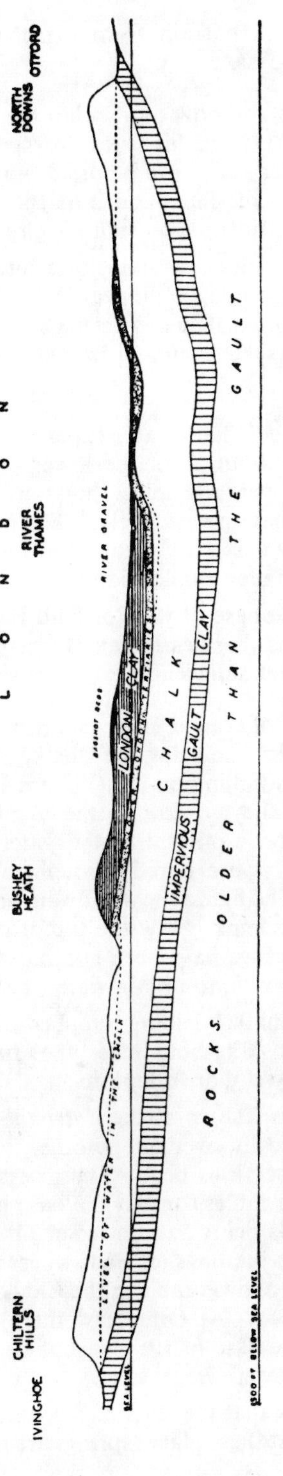

FIG. 24.—*Diagrammatic section across the London Basin to show the Water-table in the Chalk*
The vertical scale is greatly exaggerated

rubber tyres, whereas flints taken fresh from the chalk are brittle and the broken edges are as sharp as glass.

Ironstone.—The only ironstone now dug within the district is found at the top of the Middle Lias in north Oxfordshire. It is worked in open quarries under as much as 14 ft. of overburden. The ore before drying contains 22 to 30 per cent. of iron, 8 to 12 per cent. of silica, and 2 to 16 per cent. of lime. After crushing the ore is sent to the Midlands or South Wales for smelting.

Other ironstones in the district are of historic interest only. An impure carbonate was dug round St. George's Hill, near Weybridge, between 1779 and 1812, and supplied two iron mills. The ore occurs as iron-pan, from 3 to 8 in. thick, at the junction of the Bracklesham and Bagshot formations. An analysis gave 23 per cent. of iron.

Phosphatic Deposits.—The Chalk at Taplow, Bucks. contains two phosphatic bands, the upper about 8 ft., the lower 4 ft. thick, separated by about 6 ft. of chalk. The upper and lower horizons contain 18·6 and 35·6 per cent. of calcium phosphate respectively. The area within which the phosphatic deposits are known is barely three and a half miles long from north-east to south-west and under a mile wide.

The lydian stone bed at the base of the Portland Beds at Swindon rests on Kimmeridge Clay. It contains, besides lydian stone, rolled fossils which are phosphatized, but the bed is not sufficiently extensive to be of economic value.

Water Supply.—There are, of course, many sources of Water Supply in the Thames Valley district, the chief one being the Chalk. A diagrammatic section (Fig. 24, p. 57) shows how rain falling on the Chiltern Hills and North Downs collects under the Thames Valley, owing to the Gault Clay below and the Reading and London Clays above preventing the water from escaping. When the Reading and London Clays are bored through, water under pressure is found in the Chalk beneath. The figure shows how, in an area under the middle of London, the water level has sunk below the top of the Chalk as a result of over-pumping. Sometimes borings have been continued through the Chalk to considerable depths, as at Harwich, to obtain water from beneath the Gault.

Formations, other than Chalk, yielding supplies of water are the Lower Greensand, Blackheath Beds, Bagshot Beds, the Jurassic limestones and sandstones, and sandy and gravelly drift deposits.

The water-level in a rock is known as the *water-table*, and it is possible to have one or more tables vertically over one another, when pervious beds are separated by intermediate impervious beds. Thus, between Farnborough and Woolwich there are two water-tables, one in the base of the Blackheath Beds held up by the Woolwich Beds below, and a lower one in the Chalk. Again, around Bagshot there is one in the Bagshot Beds where the water is held up by the London Clay beneath, and a lower table in the Chalk. Sometimes the upper level is called a ' perched ' level. At Ottershaw there are no less than three water-tables, the highest at the base of the Bagshot Beds, the next one in the Chalk and the lowest in the Lower Greeensand.

It will be noticed in Fig. 24 that the level of the water in the Chalk touches the surface in several places. At these places springs are found. After exceptionally wet seasons the water-level rises in the Chalk and springs may overflow some distance above the usual positions and in what is normally a dry valley. These intermittent springs are called *bournes* and are known by many other names, including ' woe-waters ', because of a superstition that their flow foretells disaster. The best-known bournes are the one at Croydon and the Hertfordshire Bourne near Berkhamsted.

In dry, elevated regions, such as the Clay-with-flints areas, water is sometimes obtained from *Dew-ponds*. These are shallow ponds lined with puddled clay and straw, or cement.

IX. MAPS, PUBLICATIONS, ETC., DEALING WITH THE DISTRICT

GEOLOGICAL SURVEY MAPS AND MEMOIRS

New Series Maps and Memoirs—Scale 1 in. to 1 mile and 1:50,000

Oxford District, 1908. Also Explanatory Memoir, 2nd edition, 1926. London District (colour printed), 1927. Memoir 2nd edition 1922.

No. 204 (Biggleswade), 1949
,, 235 (Cirencester), Reprint 1946
,, 236 (Witney), Reprint 1972
,, 238 (Aylesbury), Reprint 1972
,, 239 (Hertford), Reprint 1948
,, 241 (Chelmsford), 1975
,, 254 (Henley), 1974
,, 255 (Beaconsfield), Reprint 1974
,, 256 (N. London), Reprint 1951
,, 257 (Romford), Reprint 1951
,, 266 (Marlborough), Reprint 1974
No. 267 (Hungerford), Reprint 1947
,, 268 (Reading), Reprint 1971
,, 269 (Windsor), Reprint 1948
,, 270 (S. London), Reprint 1972
,, 271 (Dartford), Reprint 1971
,, 272 (Chatham), 1951
,, 283 (Andover), Reprint 1959
,, 284 (Basingstoke), Reprint 1974
,, 285 (Aldershot), Reprint 1949
,, 286 (Reigate), Reprint 1950
,, 287 (Sevenoaks), 1971

These maps are Drift or Solid and Drift editions. A memoir describing the area has been published for most sheets.

Note: Many of the maps listed below are now out of print, but are available for public inspection in the Library of the Geological Museum.

Old Series Maps and Memoirs—Scale 1 inch to 1 mile

(*Out of print*)

(D. signified Drift and S. signifies Solid edition)

The following sheets cover parts of the area of which New Series maps have not yet been issued.

When separate quarter sheets are mentioned each quarter is a distinct map.

No. 48 N.W., N.E., S.W., S.E. (all D.).
,, 47 (S. and D.).
,, 46 N.E. (S. and D.) ; S.E. (D.) ; N.W. (S) ; S.W. (S.).
,, 45 N.E. (S. and D.) ; S.E. (S.) ; N.W. (S.) ; S.W. (S.).
,, 52 S.W. (S.).
,, 34 (S.).
,, 13 (S.).
,, 53 S.W. (S.).

A memoir is published for each of the sheets 34, 45 ; 45 S.W.; 48 N.W. and N.E.; S.W., S.E. Also for 13.

Quarter-inch to the Mile Maps

Sheets 15, 16, 19, 20 (with 24). These are Solid editions. Also Drift editions of 16 and 20 (with 24).

Six-inch Maps of the London District

These sheets cover a restricted area centred on London. They are colour printed and are numbered NI-NXIV (omitting NVII and NXI which are beyond the limits of this issue). Published in 42 quarter sheets. Area covered by each quarter sheet is six square miles.

Six-inch Maps of the London District—*continued*

NI N.W. Kenton
NI N.E. Finchley
NI S.W. Wembley
NI S.E. Hampstead
NII N.W. Tottenham
NII N.E. Higham Hill
NII S.W. Highgate
NII S.E. Stamford Hill
NIII N.W. Woodford
NIII N.E. Barkingside
NIII S.W. Leyton
NIII S.E. Ilford
NIV N.W. Willesden
NIV N.E. Paddington
NIV S.W. Acton
NIV S.E. Kensington
NV N.W. St. Pancras
NV N.E. Hackney
NV S.W. Charing Cross
NV S.E. Liverpool Street
NVI N.W. Stratford
NVI N.E. Barking
NVI S.W. Bromley-by-Bow
NVI S.E. Woolwich
NVIII N.W. Chiswick
NVIII N.E. Chelsea
NVIII S.W. Richmond
NVIII S.E. Wandsworth
NIX N.W. Clapham
NIX N.E. New Cross
NIX S.W. Balham
NIX S.E. Dulwich
NX N.W. Greenwich
NX N.E. Plumstead
NX S.W. Hither Green
NX S.E. Eltham
NXII N.W. Kingston
NXII N.E. Wimbledon
NXIII N.W. Streatham
NXIII N.E. Crystal Palace
NXIV N.W. Bromley
NXIV N.E. Chislehurst

General Memoirs

REID, C. Pleistocene Deposits of Britain, 1890.

NEWTON, E. T. Vertebrata of the Pliocene Deposits of Britain, 1891.

JUKES-BROWNE, A. J. Cretaceous Rocks of Britain : Vol. I. The Gault and Upper Greensand of England, 1900, Vol. II. The Lower and Middle Chalk of England, 1903, Vol. III. The Upper Chalk of England, 1904.

WOODWARD, H. B. Jurassic Rocks of Britain : Vol. III. The Lias of England and Wales (Yorks excepted), 1893, Vol. IV. The Lower Oolitic Rocks of England (Yorks excepted), 1894, Vol. V. The Middle and Upper Oolitic Rocks of England (Yorks excepted), 1895.

LAMPLUGH, G. W., C. B. WEDD, and J. PRINGLE. Special Reports on the Mineral Resources of Great Britain. Vol. XII. Iron Ores. Bedded Ores of the Lias, Oolites and Later Formations in England, 1920.

WOODWARD, H. B. The Geology of the London District, 2nd edition, revised by C. E. N. Bromehead, 1922.

STRAHAN, A. Geology of the Thames Valley near Goring, as illustrated by the Model in the Museum of Practical Geology, 1924.

WHITAKER, W. Geology of London and of Part of the Thames Valley, 1889, Vol. I. Descriptive Geology. Vol. II. Appendices (Well-Sections, Borings, etc.). (Covers Old Series, Sheets 1, 2 and 7.)

——Geology of the London Basin (*Mem. Geol. Surv.*, Vol. IV, Part I), 1872.

WOODWARD, H. B. Soils and Sub-soils from a Sanitary point of view ; with especial reference to London and its neighbourhood, 1897.

Memoirs on Water Supply

BLAKE, J. H. Water supply of Berkshire from underground sources, 1902.

WHITAKER, W. Water supply of Buckinghamshire and Hertfordshire from underground sources, 1921.

WHITAKER, W. and J. C. THRESH. Water supply of Essex from underground sources, 1916.
———and OTHERS. Water supply of Kent, with records of sinkings and borings, 1908.
TIDDEMAN, R. H. Water supply of Oxfordshire, with records of sinkings and borings 1910.
WHITAKER, W. Water supply of Surrey from underground sources, 1912.
———and F. H. EDMUNDS. Water supply of Wiltshire from underground sources, 1925.
BARROW, G., and L. J. WILLS. Records of London Wells, 1913.
BUCHAN, S. Water Supply of the County of London, 1938.

Short List of Other Works

ARKELL, W. J. The Jurassic System in Great Britain, 1933.
BARROW, G. Some Future Work for the Geologists' Association. *Proc. Geol. Assoc.*, vol. 30, 1919.
BOSWELL, P. G. H. The Contacts of Geology : The Ice Age and Early Man in Britain. *Reports Brit. Assoc.* for 1932, 1932.
DAVIES, A. M., and J. PRINGLE. On Two Deep Borings at Calvert Station (N. Bucks.) and on the Palaeozoic Floor north of the Thames. *Quart. Journ. Geol. Soc.*, vol. 69, 1913.
DAVIES, G. M. Geological Excursions round London, 1914.
DAVIS, A. G., and G. F. ELLIOTT. The Palaeogeography of the London Clay Sea. *Proc. Geol. Assoc.*, vol. 68, 1958.
DEWEY, H. The Palaeolithic Deposits of the Lower Thames Valley. *Quart. Journ. Geol. Soc.*, vol. 88, 1932.
GILBERT, C. J. On the Occurrence of Extensive Deposits of High-level Sands and Gravel resting upon the Chalk at Little Heath near Berkhamsted. *Quart. Journ. Geol. Soc.*, vol. 75, 1920.
HARMER, F. W. The Pliocene Deposits of the East of England—Part II. The Crag of Essex (Waltonian) and its relation to that of Suffolk and Norfolk. *Quart. Journ. Geol. Soc.*, vol. 56, 1900.
———On the Origin of Certain Cañon-like Valleys associated with Lake-like Areas of Depression. *Quart. Journ. Geol. Soc.*, vol. 63, 1907.
KENNARD, A. S. The Crayford Brickearths. *Proc. Geol. Assoc.*, vol. 55, 1944.
PRESTWICH, J. On the Probable Age of the London Clay and its Relations to the Hampshire and Paris Tertiary System. *Quart. Journ. Geol. Soc.*, vol. 3, 1847.
———On the Main Points of Structure and the probable Age of the Bagshot Sands, and on their presumed equivalents in Hampshire and France. *Quart. Journ. Geol. Soc.*, vol. 3, 1847.
———On the Structure of the Strata between the London Clay and the Chalk in the London and Hampshire Tertiary Systems—Part I. *Quart. Journ. Geol. Soc.* vol. 6, 1850 ; Part II, ibid., vol. 10, 1854 ; Part III, ibid., vol. 8, 1852.
SANDFORD, K. S. The River-Gravels of the Oxford District. *Quart. Journ. Geol. Soc.*, vol. 80, 1924.
SHERLOCK, R. L. The Superficial Deposits of S. Bucks and S. Herts and the Old Course of the Thames. *Proc. Geol. Assoc.*, vol. 35, 1924.
———AND OTHERS. Discussion on the Alleged Pliocene of Bucks and Herts. *Proc. Geol. Assoc.*, vol. 40, 1929.
STRAHAN, A. Form of the Palaeozoic Platform. Pres. Address. *Quart. Journ. Geol. Soc.*, vol. 69, 1913.
WHITE, H. J. O. On the Origin of the High-level Gravel with Triassic Debris adjoining the Valley of the Upper Thames. *Proc. Geol. Assoc.*, vol. 15, 1899.
WOOLDRIDGE, S. W. The Pliocene History of the London Basin. *Proc. Geol. Assoc.*, vol. 38, 1927.
———Some Aspects of the Physiography of the Thames Valley in Relation to the Ice-Age and Early Man. *Proc. Prehist. Soc.*, vol. 23, 1957.
WRIGLEY, A. The Faunal Succession in the London Clay, illustrated in some New Exposures near London. *Proc. Geol. Assoc.*, vol. 51, 1940.

Additional References to 1975

BRISTOW, C. R. and COX, F. C. 1973. The Gipping Till: a reappraisal of East Anglian glacial stratigraphy. *Jl. Geol. Soc. Lond.*, vol. 129, 1–37.

COWPERTHWAITE, I. A., FITCH, F. J., MILLER, J. A., MITCHELL, J. G. and ROBERTSON, R. 1972. Sedimentation, petrogenesis and radio isotopic age of the Cretaceous fuller's earth of Southern England. *Clay Miner.*, vol. 9, 309–327.

CURRY, D. 1965. The Palaeogene beds of south-east England. *Proc. Geol. Assoc.*, vol. 76, 151–174.

———1966. Problems of correlation in the Anglo-Paris-Belgian basin. *Proc. Geol. Assoc.*, vol. 77, 437–468.

HEY, R. W. 1965. Highly quartzose pebble gravels in the London basin. *Proc. Geol. Assoc.*, vol. 76, 403–420.

HOLMES, S. C. A. 1971. The geological mapper and the employment of his results as illustrated in some areas of southern England. *Proc. Geol. Assoc.*, vol. 82, 161–186.

LOVEDAY, J. 1962. Plateau deposits of the southern Chiltern Hills. *Proc. Geol. Assoc.*, vol. 73, 83–102.

OWEN, H. G. 1971. The stratigraphy of the Gault in the Thames estuary, and its bearing on the Mesozoic tectonic history of the area. *Proc. Geol. Assoc.*, vol. 82, 187–208.

SANDFORD, K. S. 1965. Notes on the gravels of the upper Thames flood plain between Lechlade and Dorchester. *Proc. Geol. Assoc.*, vol. 76, 61–76.

SYLVESTER BRADLEY, P. C. and FORD, T. D. (Eds.). 1968. The Geology of the East Midlands. (Leicester: Leicester University Press).

THOMASSON, A. J. 1961. Some aspects of the drift deposits and geomorphology of south-east Hertfordshire. *Proc. Geol. Assoc.*, vol. 72, 287–302.

WOOLDRIDGE, S. W. 1960. The Pleistocene succession in the London Basin. *Proc. Geol. Assoc.*, vol. 71, 113–129.

WYMER, J. J. 1975. Clactonian and Acheulian industries in Britain – their chronology and significance. *Proc. Geol. Assoc.*, vol. 85, 391–422.

Dd 289686 K48

Printed in England for Her Majesty's Stationery Office by
Ebenezer Baylis & Son Ltd. Leicester and London